## Key Stage 3 English
## Literacy Strategy Workbooks

These 3 books have been <u>written specifically</u> to
follow the Literacy Strategy for KS3.

Each page has questions covering a Teaching Objective from the Literacy Strategy.
Tips have also been included for some of the more difficult questions.

And there's even the odd ever-so-nearly entertaining bit,
just to help keep you awake.

## What CGP is all about

Our sole aim here at CGP is to produce the highest quality
books — carefully written, immaculately presented
and dangerously close to being funny.

Then we work our socks off to get them out to you
— at the cheapest possible prices.

# Contents

# Contents

Published by CGP

*Contributors:*
Adrian Burke
Mark Chambers
Alex Cherian
Vivienne Crawford
Taissa Csáky
Mary Drayton
Gemma Hallam
Simon Little
Tammy Nichols
Alison Palin
Glenn Rogers
Alison Sagrott
Julie Schofield
Jenny Watson
Chrissy Williams

*Also Starring:*
a medium sized goat with a tuba

*With Thanks to:*
Rosemary Cartwright for the proofreading.

ISBN: 978 1 84146 135 9

Groovy website: www.cgpbooks.co.uk
Printed by Elanders Ltd, Newcastle upon Tyne.

Based on the classic CGP style created by Richard Parsons.

# Getting the Right Vowels

**Q1** Copy down this list of words. Next to each word, write down as many words as you can which rhyme with the word and which end with the same letters.

a) farm

b) bee

c) short

d) pea

e) day

f) caught

g) fate

h) eight

i) bought

j) calm

k) rain

l) coat

m) bone

**Q2** Write out these sentences, putting in the missing words from the box:

> thief  weight  *sight*  deceive  niece  received  grey
>
> *fight*  piece  believed  relief  mail  survey  sails  weighing

*Tip — in each sentence, the missing words have the same vowel sounds, spelt in the same way.*

a) Give my ...... a ...... of cake.

b) According to the ......, women are just as likely to wear ... clothes as men.

c) I ...... it was a ......, but to my ...... I was wrong.

d) Please ...... me your price list for ...... and surfboards.

e) We acted as soon as we ...... the letter and certainly did not intend to ...... anyone.

f) Don't lose ...... of what's important — let's continue to ...... for justice.

g) ...... yourself every day won't affect your .......

*Many words have vowels that are not clearly pronounced in ordinary conversation, but which mustn't be missed out when you write the words down.*

**Q3** The writer of this article has missed out several vowels. Write out the article without any spelling mistakes. Underline the vowels which you've added.

> **Local MP and busnessman wed on warmest day this summer**
>
> *A local member of Parlament and a well-known busnessman tied the knot in an elaborate ceremony at St George's Cathedral yesterday. The bride, whose designer dress was studded with dimonds, arrived in a horse-drawn carrige as tempratures soared to 30°C. The groom said he was looking forward to a long and happy marrige. When asked about living with a politican, he joked, "Well, I've already got my own secretry, but maybe one day I'll have my own Secretry of State as well."*

# start, tart, cart, f... err, can't think of any more...

Sometimes it can be tricky to get the correct spellings for vowel sounds. Unfortunately, there's no easy way around it except to learn them. So that's just what you'll have to do. Yippee...

# Plurals

*Sometimes you need to do more than just add an **s** to form plurals.*

**Q1** Match each plural-making instruction a) to f) with the correct description from the pile. Use the big list of examples to help you figure it all out.

a)  add s

b)  add es

c)  cut off f, add ves

d)  cut off fe, add ves

e)  cut off y, add ies

f)  do nothing at all

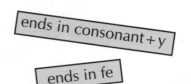
ends in consonant + y

ends in f

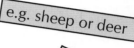
e.g. sheep or deer

ends in fe

ends in s, x, ch, or sh

ends in e

Examples to help you:

game → games     church → churches     sheep → sheep

pony → ponies     calf → calves     life → lives

*Most words ending in **o** just add **s** to make the plural.*

**Q2** Write out these sentences, putting in the correct word from the box each time.

a)  Do you ever go to the school ...?

b)  They sold ... and other musical instruments.

c)  Have you brought any ... with you?

d)  I sing alto, but Sally and Karen are ....

photos    sopranos

pianos    discos

the plural of sheep

*Some words ending in **o**, including "potato" and "tomato", add **es** to make the plural.*

**Q3** Write these sentences out, changing the plural forms into singular forms.

a)  Our heroes ate mangoes on the volcanoes.

b)  The ships lost their cargoes when they were hit by torpedoes.

c)  The heavenly echoes made the angels drop their haloes.

*Tip: all the words ending in oes are like "potatoes" and "tomatoes" — the singular form ends in o.*

**Q4** Write these sentences out, changing the words that end in **y** into plural forms:

a)  The donkey kicked me in the kidney.

b)  Their jersey got stuck in the chimney.

c)  The boy found a way of mending the toy.

d)  We all had an ice lolly.

e)  Bring your diary with you.

f)  The survey showed what people want.

**Q5** Write down the plural forms of these words:

*Tip: use a dictionary if you need to...*

a) larva   b) formula   c) criterion   d) phenomenon   e) bacterium

# There's nothing worse than running out of plu-ral...

Lots of lovely spelling rules here, so get learning because <u>spelling rules</u>. Ha ha, geddit? Nevermind...

# Word Endings

**Q1**  Before adding an ending to a word, you may need to change the word a bit.
Write out these sentences.  Use a word formed from the word in brackets to fill in the gap.

a)  She was ... and laughing.  *(smile)*

b)  I ... dressing up when I was little.  *(love)*

c)  They ... us with office furniture.  *(supply)*

d)  She looks even ... than usual.  *(pale)*

e)  We ... a drink and some crisps.  *(share)*

f)  The weather was ... than ever.  *(grey)*

g)  I was only ... .  *(joke)*

h)  You know I care about your ....  *(happy)*

**Q2**  Some endings are easy to confuse.
Write out these sentences, using **ible** or **able** to complete the unfinished words:

a)  It's incred... that he behaved so badly.

b)  Your cheek is unbeliev....

c)  Your writing is only just leg....

d)  The whole essay was barely read....

e)  It was terr... to see him so ill.

f)  We all felt utterly miser....

g)  It's poss... that I made a mistake.

h)  He's a very reli... chap.

i)  Who's respons... for this mess?

j)  There are several identifi... problems here.

k)  The meal was completely ined....

l)  It was a thoroughly enjoy... evening.

**Q3**  Write out these sentences using the endings in the box to complete the unfinished words.

| ician | ssion | sion | otion | ation | ition | tion |
|-------|-------|------|-------|-------|-------|------|

a)  Pay atten...... while I tell you which direc...... to go in.

b)  They're demanding an explan...... about the accommod...... mix-up.

c)  The team deserved prom...... after putting so much energy and em...... into their game.

d)  One brother was a polit......, one was a mus......, and the other was an electr.......

e)  The final discu...... was about oppre...... in various countries.

f)  In conclu......, the state of confu...... which followed the deci...... has not yet ended.

g)  The compet...... hasn't finished but they're in a very good pos.......

**Q4**

a)  Put these words into two lists, with the headings **ends in "ant"** and **ends in "ent"**:

   *accountant   important   adjacent   independent   ingredient   pleasant*
   *component   current   servant   consultant   relevant   currant*

b)  Write a sentence about **ant<u>s</u>** for each of the words ending in **ant**.

   *For "accountant" you could put "The accountant's office was covered in ants."*

c)  Write a sentence about **Eve 'n' Tom** for each of the words ending in **ent**.

   *For "current" you could put "Eve 'n' Tom want to change their current account."*

# Prefixes

*Prefixes are the bits at the beginnings of words which give you a clue to their meaning.*

Q1   Match up each prefix with the right meaning and an example word:

a) anti-   b) bi-   c) contra-   d) de-   e) inter-   f) mis-   g) non-   h) re-   i) sub-

> Meanings:       between          against                      again
>         wrong / bad      two      under      undo / remove      not

> Examples:       interval      replay      antifreeze      bicycle      de-stress
>    non-governmental      contradict      misunderstanding      sub-zero

Q2   Write a sentence for each word in Q1.

Q3   Write a list of words formed by matching up each word here with the correct prefix:

a)   logical

b)   edible

c)   believable

d)   possible

e)   refutable

> **Prefixes**
> il-
> im-
> in-
> ir-
> un-

Q4   Write a sentence for each word in Q3.

Q5   Sort the words in the box into groups, under the following headings a to h.

a)   distance          e)   round / around

b)   again             f)   listening / hearing

c)   two               g)   life / living

d)   across            h)   Internet / computers

*The first part of each word gives a clue about the meaning — and what heading it should go under.*

> television  replay  circle  bicycle  transatlantic  biology  repeat
> telescope  circumstances  transfer  bifocals  cybercafé  transmit
> circumference  bilingual  circulate  translate  telephone  audience
> audible  auditorium  resend  biography  cyberspace

## Inter mission — James Bond takes a tea break...

I <u>love</u> prefixes. I just <u>can't get enough</u> of them. That's because they help you to guess what the word means. Go learn the common prefixes and their meanings and you'll <u>learn to love them</u> too.

# <u>*Using Apostrophes*</u>

**Q1**  You use apostrophes to show who something (or someone) belongs to.
Write out these sentences, adding the apostrophe in the right place:

a)  Pass Mums bag over.

b)  Bills football kit is filthy.

c)  Ann is Elizabeths mum.

d)  Leave Jacks things alone.

e)  Mrs Jacksons class is taking assembly today.

> Apostrophe before or after the **s**?
> *Pick up your **brother's** shoes = the shoes belonging to your **brother**.*
> *Pick up your **brothers'** shoes = the shoes belonging to your **brothers**.*

**Q2**  Write down these sentences.  After each one, write down how many
sisters are being talked about.  (It might be one, or more than one.)

a)  My sister's boyfriend is very nice.

b)  She borrowed her sister's shoes.

c)  He used to steal his sisters' sweets.

d)  She's my sister's best friend.

**Q3**  You use apostrophes in words like **isn't** and **can't** which have letters missed out.
Match up each of the short forms on the left with the correct long form from the right:

a)  you're     e)  it's      i)  don't       *they are   I have   you are*

b)  isn't      f)  they're   j)  he's        *is not   are not   cannot*

c)  aren't     g)  I've      k)  wouldn't    *it is / it has   have not   do not*

d)  can't      h)  haven't                   *he is / he has   would not*

**Q4**  Don't confuse **its** with **it's**.  Write out these sentences, adding **it's** or **its** in the gaps:

a)  ... a shame about the school's old guinea pig.  = **It is** a shame.

b)  Our dog ate ... old one.  = **belonging to it** (the school)

c)  ... got a new one now.  = **It** (the school) **has** got a new one.

**Q5**  Write down these sentences, adding an apostrophe where necessary:

a)  Take your things with you.        *If the s is just a plural form, you don't need an apostrophe.*

b)  Give me Janes homework.           *Add 's to irregular plurals like "men" and "women" to show that something belongs to the men or women.*

c)  Copy the work out of Toms book.

d)  The other childrens parents were very nice.

e)  The mens changing rooms are over there.

f)  Dont forget your glasses.

# Words That Sound the Same or Similar

**Q1**    Copy out this conversation, putting in the correct word from the box below:

a)    "Where ... you earlier?" said Mum.

b)    "I was ... all afternoon," said Jane.

c)    "... was your brother, then?" said Mum.

d)    "He went to see Chrissie."

e)    "... Chrissie?"

f)    "She's his new girlfriend.  Look — ...they are.  ... just coming up the drive now.

g)    "... is the electric guitar?" said Mum.

h)    "It's mine," said Jane.  "Didn't we tell you we'd started a band?  Look — Chrissie and Dan have brought ... drum kits.  Mum — where are you going?"

i)    "Somewhere where I can ... myself think," said Mum.  "Don't wait up."

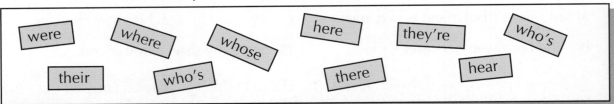

were    where    whose    here    they're    who's    their    who's    there    hear

**Q2**    Write out these sentences, choosing one word from the pair in brackets to fill in each gap.

a)    Take my ... — don't do it.  (advice / advise)

b)    You still need some more ....  (practice / practise)

c)    He doesn't have a ... to drive.  (licence / license)

d)    Could you be ... for a moment?  (quite / quiet)

it sounds like "bone"

e)    Having a baby will definitely ... your social life.  (affect / effect)

f)    It's ... obvious that this is a bad idea.  (quite / quiet)

g)    She couldn't pay him back because she'd just ... herself a designer dress.  (brought / bought)

h)    I've ... you those books you wanted from the library.  (brought / bought )

i)    I'll ... him not to go.  (advice / advise)

j)    He ...d the drums in the front room every night.  (practice / practise)

k)    Tricia's taxi is ...d to carry four passengers.  (licence / license)

l)    Name one ... of removing the cover.  (affect / effect)

## "where are you?"  "No thanks, sheep bring me out in a rash"...

It's <u>really easy</u> to ~~right~~ write the wrong one (Aha, see?). You never know ~~wear~~ where (ah... look at that!) it's going to happen next. So <u>don't be moomin</u> — learn the words and <u>be careful</u>. Be <u>very, very</u> careful...

# Spellings That Keep Popping Up

**Q1** Get used to reviewing your writing and checking for spelling mistakes. Write out this political paragraph, correcting the misspellings:

*Mystery Hint — the number of wrongly spelt words is somewhere between 7 and 10...*

*Yesterday the goverment was still refusing to comment specificly on the matter. However, a spokesman said: "The Prime Minister continues to support the Secretary of State. We have no reason to believe that he acted inapproprietely in any way. Furthemore, he is an experienced and valued member of the cabinet." Supporters of the Secretary of State have reaffirmed their comittment to ensuring that he remains in office. Unfortunatly, however, this issue is not likely to dissapear quickly, and observers are warning that a new stratagy may be nesessary. The atmosphere in parliament yesterday afternoon was rowdy; opposition MPs called for explanations, and there were allegations of an "outrageous cover-up".*

**Q2** Write out the sentences, filling in the gaps. To do this, choose a word from the box on the left and a word from the box on the right, and either join them together or keep them separate.

a) Let me know if I can do ... to help.

b) "Thanks again for everything." "...."

c) Does ... want a game of chess?

d) Do you want ... chicken?

e) He doesn't play in the band ....

f) Choose ... card from the pack.

g) He said ... that were really unkind.

h) There's ... at the door.

i) We've been dealing with this problem for ....

j) ... you really annoy me.

| any... <br> some... | **+** | ...one  ...time <br> ...thing  ...times <br> ...things  ...more |
|---|---|---|

**Q3** Next to each word, copy down the right definition:

a) here — they are
b) there — what you do with clothes
c) where — what you get from a tree
d) hear — used in questions such as "... you like a cup of tea?"
e) would — a place nearby
f) they're — a place further away
g) wear — what you do with your ears
h) wood — used for asking questions about position or place

**Q4** There are six spelling mistakes in this list. Write out the list, correcting the words which are wrong. Use a dictionary to check any words which you're not sure about.

a) disappointing
b) begining
c) consequents
d) imaginary
e) potential
f) technology
g) strenghth
h) persuasion
i) interupting
j) embarassed
k) ceiling
l) mariage

**Q5** Write a sentence using each word in Q4. Make sure you use the correct spelling.

Keep your own list of words which you find difficult to spell. Check in a dictionary that you've written them down correctly. Keep practising them and you'll improve — effort pays off. Oh — where's my tip box gone? I feel all naked. Quick, turn the page... I'm going red.

# *Thinking About Patterns in Words*

**Q1** Write out these groups of words. For each group, first write down how the words are similar, and then write down what this tells you about their meanings.

a) audiovisual visualise vision television visionary

b) nutritious nutrition nutrient

c) creation creative create creator recreate

d) argue argument arguable arguably argumentative

e) necessary necessitate necessity necessarily

f) participate participation participants

g) evaluation value undervalued revalue re-evaluate

h) know knowing knowledge knowledgeable unknowingly

**Q2** From each group of words in Q1, choose the word which (in your opinion) is the most difficult to spell. Now write a sentence containing that word.

**Q3** Write out these sentences. Fill in the gaps with the word "**differ**" or a word related to it:

a) The two things are completely ....

b) We have ... views on this subject.

c) What's the ... between these two photos?

d) How do your opinions ...?

**Q4** Write out these sentences. Fill in the gaps with the word "**weak**" or a word related to it:

a) Chocolate is my main ....

b) He said his resolve would not ....

c) The old lady was growing ... every day.

d) Lorries aren't allowed along the High Street because of the ... bridge.

**Q5** Write out these sentences. Fill in the gaps with the word "**cent**" or a word related to it:

a) A ... is a hundredth of a dollar.

b) He played a Roman ... in the school play.

c) The position of women changed significantly during the 20th ....

d) The school recently celebrated its ....

---

**"Tartan, gingham, check..."** *Don't mind me, just thinking about patterns in words...*
When you come across a new word, see if you recognise any bits of it. That way you can see clues to its meaning <u>and</u> a way of remembering the spelling. Two tips for the price of one. Bargain.

# Some Long Words and Some Odd Words

**Q1** Write down these words. Next to each word, write down a shorter word contained in it:

a) globalisation ⟶ *global*

b) unimportant

c) statistician

d) accountability

e) reconstruction

f) callousness

g) transportation

h) characteristic

*Don't try to be smart. You can't use tiny words like "is" or "sat".*

**Q2** Some words are difficult to spell because they were originally from a different language.

a) Write down ten words that refer to food which are used in English but were originally foreign words. (NB: only one type of pasta is allowed)

b) Write down the language or area which each word originally came from. Use a dictionary if you need to.

**Q3** Write out these sentences, filling in each of the gaps with a word from the box:

| biro | sellotape | diesel | sandwich | hoovering |
|------|-----------|--------|----------|-----------|

a) Does your car take petrol or ...?

b) My pen's run out — can I borrow your ...?

c) I didn't hear the phone because I was ....

d) I'll make you a ... for your lunch.

e) Have you got any ...? This page is torn.

*Some of these words were originally people's names — the biro pen was invented by a Mr Biro. Some of them were made up to be used as product names or trademarks.*

**Q4** Acronyms are words which are made up of the initial letters of a phrase. Write down the acronyms or abbreviations which are used instead of these phrases:

a) North Atlantic Treaty Organization

b) light amplification by stimulated emission of radiation

c) compact disc

d) bovine spongiform encephalopathy

e) non-governmental organization

f) quasi-autonomous non-governmental organization

g) radio detecting and ranging

# Shhhh — we're hunting the elusive quango...

It's never-ending, this spelling business. The problem with the words featured on this page is that there aren't any helpful rules to learn and remember. You've just got to learn the spellings. Bummer.

# How Letters Affect Each Other

*Letters can sound different depending on the other letters near them.*

*See how the <u>p</u> on the end of <u>grip</u> has been doubled — otherwise it would say "griping".*

**Stop griping about spellings and start gripping your pen!**

*"Grip" contains a short vowel sound — it rhymes with "snip" and "trip".*
*"Gripe" contains a long vowel sound — it rhymes with "snipe" and "tripe" (yum).*

**Q1**  Write these words in two separate lists, under the headings **short vowel** and **long vowel**:

hoped   hopped   mopped   moped   pined   pinned

**Q2**  Write out these sentences, using the correct words from the lists in Q1:

a)  Auntie Nasty ...... me against the wall and said, "You ...... around on your pogo stick right after I'd ...... the floor."

*Tip: to keep that vowel sounding short, remember to double the following consonant before adding the ending.*

b)  The dog ...... for weeks when Pankha went to college.  We ...... she would cheer up but she ...... around the house for ages.

**Q3**  Write down these words.  Next to each one, write down the word formed by adding the ending shown in brackets.

a)  beg (ed)      d)  wet (est)

b)  big (er)      e)  tug (ing)

c)  stop (ed)     f)  pat (ed)

**Q4**  Write out these sentences, filling in the gaps with words formed from the words and endings in the boxes below.

a)  Stop … and think.

b)  I'm fed up with your constant … — you're always finding fault with everything.

c)  He's very … about the decision.

d)  There was a lot of … voting.

e)  We … on the grass.

*Remember — with words like "picnic", change c to ck before adding ed, er, or ing.*

| **Words** | **Endings** |
|---|---|
| panic     picnic   stoic    tactic    critic | ing    ism    al    ed |

# Love letters affect me the most...

If an **-ing** word has a <u>short vowel</u> when you say it, it's spelt with a <u>double consonant</u> e.g. sho<u>pp</u>ing.
If it's a <u>long vowel</u>, then it's a <u>single consonant</u>, e.g. jou<u>st</u>ing.  The excitement just keeps building...

# Applying Spelling Rules

**Q1**  *"Do I know a rule which can help me to spell the word?"*
Write down answers to the following questions.

a) Oops — I wanted to write **snipping**, but I've written **sniping**. What have I forgotten to do?

b) I wanted to write **hoping**, but I've written **hopeing**. Aaargh! What have I forgotten to do?

c) I wanted to write **quiet**, but I've written **qiet**. D'oh! What have I forgotten to do this time?

d) I wanted to write the plural of **dog**, but I've written **dog's**. Why's this **wrong**?

e) I've written down **bashful** and I can't decide if it's correct or not. How can I work it out?

f) I wanted to write **pianos**, but I've gone and written **pianoes**. What rule have I forgotten?

g) Write down some words which really end in **-oes** in the plural.

**Q2**  *Can I think of other words — or bits of words — which will help me to spell this word?*
Write down answers to the following questions.

a) Kate wanted to write **cell** but she's written **sell**. Which other words
(or bits of words) could help her to remember which is which?

b) Abdulmalik wanted to write **interrupt** but he's gone and left out an **r**. Which
other words (or bits of words) will help him to spell it correctly?

c) Beth wanted to write **deceive** but she's made a mistake and put "ie" instead
of "ei". Which other words contain **cei**?

d) How can Steven remember whether to put one **s** or two in **disappear**?
Is it single or double **p**?

**Q3**  *Does the way I say the word make it easy to remember the spelling?*
Write a sentence containing each of the words below. (Write one sentence for each word.)

a) pron**ou**nce

b) pron**u**nciation

c) **spe**cific

d) **Pa**cific

e) **br**ought

f) **b**ought

g) **per**spective

h) **pro**spective

i) **f**ree

j) **th**ree

k) **pre**requisite

l) defin**i**te

m) February

n) per**h**aps

*Use a dictionary if you aren't sure of the meanings of any of these words.*

---

## Some classic spellings here — all my favourites...

Dictionaries and spellcheckers are dead useful — but you <u>won't</u> always be able to use them.
That's why you need to know a few <u>spelling patterns</u>. <u>Learn them</u> and be prepared to <u>use them</u>.

# Personal Spelling Strategies

*You can break words up into chunks so that they are easier to remember.*

Q1  For each word on the left below, there is a word on the right with a matching chunk.

| | |
|---|---|
| ne cess ary | inter link |
| inter est ing | lous y |
| mis cell an eous | further more |
| em barr ass | cell phone |
| jea lous | ne cess itate |
| more over | ass |

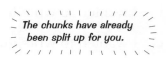
*The chunks have already been split up for you.*

a)  Write down the pairs of words, underlining the parts which are the same.

b)  For each of the words on the left, write one sentence.

Q2  *You can write down sentences which act as memory-joggers.*

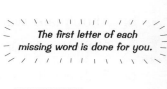
*The first letter of each missing word is done for you.*

a)  Put one of the words on the right into each of these sentences:

   i)   Sepa**rat**e the r... from the others.

   ii)  They've got a d... in the gar**den**.

   iii) M... goes to second**ary** school.

   iv)  En, Vi, Ron — m... that care about the environ**men**t.

men
rat
den
Mary

b)  In each sentence, underline the letters which act as a memory-jogger.

c)  What's the fancy word for memory-joggers like these which help you learn things?

Q3  Write down 8 words which you find difficult to spell. For each of these words, either break the word into chunks, as in Q1, or write down a short sentence which acts as a memory-jogger, or draw a picture which will help you remember the spelling.

# Personally, I spell it S-T-R-A-T-E-G-I-E-S...

Writing long words can be a bit daunting — but don't panic. Look for ways of breaking them up.
Maybe one of the chunks would fit well with a nice little memory-jogger. Suck it and see...

# Personal Spelling Strategies

*To help you spell some words, think of other words which end in the same way.*

**Q1** | Look at this long list of words:

deceive delicious ease fantastic come glove lover plastic cover variety
frustration rover tough smother station Dover brother malicious narration
piety some conceive rough drastic enough other tease sobriety society
propriety elastic love dove mother receive please capricious

a) Write the words out in groups, so that all the words in each group rhyme **and** end with the same letters.

b) In each group, put a circle around the word that **you** can spell most easily.

**Q2** | Write out the words below, in five groups. The words in each group should all end with the same letters **and** be similar in another way as well (say how they are similar).

continuous boxer dentist singing harder worker typing
therapist dancing easier photographer angrier working
windsurfing linguist economist jealous friendlier redder
miscellaneous lexicographer outrageous

*Sometimes the pronunciation of one word can help you to remember how to spell other words.*

**Q3** | Write down the word which is being defined in each of these sentences.

a) to say you no longer wish to work in a place
b) If you feel ...... to something, you accept that it is happening, although you do not like it.
c) a drawing or plan which shows what something should look like
d) someone who decides how clothes, rooms, or buildings should look
e) someone who takes pictures with a camera
f) the art of taking pictures with a camera
g) an idea or story that is based on imagination rather than fact
h) if you ......, you think about something which is very unlikely
   and pretend that it is really happening
i) the line where the land appears to meet the sky
j) if you broaden your ......, you try to experience something new
k) to organise all the different activities and people involved in an event,
   so that it is successful
l) not unusual or not remarkable
m) an extra person or thing
n) used for describing an extra person or thing
o) if you ...... in a particular type of activity or knowledge, you are particularly good at it
p) important; with a particular value or function

# Spelling counts — or is it numbers that count...

So basically, a good way to remember how to spell a tricky word is to think of a word that's spelt in a similar way. It really does work too, honest. Or your money back, etc. etc... Oh look — the section's over.

# Language Families

*Sometimes people can tell who you are related to by the fact that you have the same looks as your relatives. Words have families too — often these families are linked to particular places.*

**Q1** Match up each language family with the correct place(s):

| | | | |
|---|---|---|---|
| a) | Latin | i) | Greece |
| b) | Greek | ii) | Norway, Sweden, Denmark, Iceland, Finland |
| c) | Celtic | iii) | Rome |
| d) | Scandinavian | iv) | Scotland and Ireland |

**Q2** Match each word a) to d) with its relative from the same language family on the right:

| | | | |
|---|---|---|---|
| a) | groove (Dutch family) | i) | dekko |
| b) | confetti (Italian family) | ii) | cabinet |
| c) | pukka (Indian family) | iii) | boom |
| d) | ballet (French family) | iv) | spaghetti |

*Think about what the word actually looks like. Think about how it's pronounced too.*

**Q3** From their meanings, match up each word on the left to the correct language family:

| | | | |
|---|---|---|---|
| a) | korma | i) | French |
| b) | restaurant | ii) | Indian |
| c) | stiletto | iii) | Celtic |
| d) | tweed | iv) | Italian |

**Q4** Look up the meanings of these words, and match them up to their families. It's quite difficult.

| | | | |
|---|---|---|---|
| a) | crag, cairn, loch, clan, glen | i) | Latin |
| b) | medium, album, circus, genius, pendulum | ii) | Greek |
| c) | crisis, myth, periscope, theatre, church | iii) | Celtic |
| d) | skill, ragged, snare, root | iv) | Scandinavian |

*You can also spot links between words by looking at how they grow from common starting points, which are called **roots**.*

**Q5** Look at the Latin root '**struct**', and make three new words from the following combinations.

> con
> de       +    **struct**    +    ion
> in

**Q6** What do you think **-struct** means? (Remember, it doesn't actually exist as a word on its own.)

## *Words have families too... awww, I think I'm going to cry...*

Quite a tricky old page, this one. But the basic gist is that a <u>lot</u> of the words we use come from different languages. You can <u>guess</u> the meaning of different words which have the <u>same root</u>.

# Working Out Meanings

Q1    Look at this sentence.  Then say which of the statements a) to d) are true.

*With a sudden angry twist to his mouth, Charlie paused ominously.*

a)    You can look at other words in the sentence to figure out the meaning of a new word.

b)    Pausing means that Charlie is calm.

c)    'Ominous' means an evil or frightening thing might happen soon.

d)    Working out the meaning of an unknown word from the surrounding words is called getting the meaning from the context.

*Sometimes if we know **where** a word comes from, or what the*
***root** of the word is, we can also figure out the meaning.*

Q2    Look at the first two syllables of **"ominously"** — omin.

a)    Change the second vowel to make a new word, then look up this word in a dictionary and write down the definition.

b)    Is this word the root word of **"ominously"**?

*If you couldn't figure out the meaning of the word **"ominously"** from the **context** (the meaning of other words surrounding it), or the **etymology** (the root of the word and where the word comes from), you might need to look at the different **parts** of the word:*

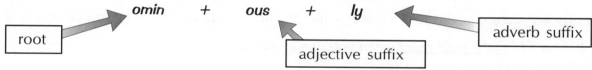

omin    +    ous    +    ly

root

adjective suffix

adverb suffix

Q3    What's the special English term for figuring out a word by thinking about its root and where it comes from?

Q4    Write down four other words that end in 'ly'.

Q5    Words from which word class end in 'ly'?

a)    adjectives (words which describe a noun)

b)    verbs (words which mean an action)

c)    adverbs (words which describe a verb)

d)    nouns (words which name a thing a person or a place)

Q6    Which of the following does "ominously" describe?

a)    the way Charlie paused

b)    Charlie

c)    the angry twist of Charlie's mouth

d)    the mouth

# Context and Idiom

**Q1** Match up the following uses of the word **groom** to the definitions below.

a) The groom stood quietly in the stable.

b) The girl was very well groomed.

c) The groom stood nervously waiting for the ceremony to start.

d) Don't come back until you are properly groomed!

> Groom (*noun*) — a person in charge of horses.
> Groom (*noun*) — the man who gets married at a wedding ceremony.
> Groom (*verb*) — to make a person look smart and tidy.

**Q2** In Q1 above, how did you decide which definition went with which use of **groom**?

**Q3** Write a sentence with the word **play** used three times — twice as a verb and once as a noun.

**Q4** Copy out statements a) to c) and use the example sentences to help you complete them.

*It's hard to __make ends meet__ when you're a student.*

a) To make ends meet means to…

*She's __all heart__.*

b) To be all heart means to…

*Don't __rake over old coals.__ What's done is done.*

c) To rake over old coals means to…

**Q5** The phrases in Q4 are known as **idiomatic phrases.** For each of these statements about idiomatic phrases, write down whether it's true or false:

a) these words won't necessarily make sense individually

b) the words have to be understood as part of a bigger sentence / context

c) the words and their real meanings are not always logical

d) these words have to rhyme

**Q6** Ask as many people as you can to help you compile an idiomatic phrase list of phrases using the word 'dig' — dig deep and find as many as you can.

Come along, Daisy. You're blocking that man's tip.

**Don't be fooled into bla bla … it's all to … ntext…**

Cop … … iom. When you
co … across … … dle in th … ay of this. Cool.

# Words, Phrases and Clauses

Q1    Nouns, adjectives, verbs, prepositions and adverbs are all known as:

a) complicated words    b) word classes    c) synonyms    d) idioms

Q2    Write a definition for each of the terms a) to e), just to prove you can.

a) nouns    b) adjectives    c) prepositions    d) verbs    e) adverbs

Q3    When you look at the order of words in a sentence, you are thinking about:

a) syntax    b) morphology    c) context    d) description

*Mmm, it's hard.  Your answers from Page 15 might help you.*

*A set of words **without a verb** is called a **phrase**.  A **noun phrase** is a set of words, without a verb, which does the job of a **noun** — i.e. it names something.*

Q4    Which of these phrases is **not** a noun phrase?  It's quite tricky.

a)  Dad's trousers

b)  The purple velvet trousers

c)  The trousers on the flag pole

d)  The terrible trousers

e)  I like trousers

f)  My other camouflage trousers

*A clause is a set of words **which has a verb** in it.*

Q5    Pair up a clause from column A and a clause from column B to produce three full sentences, each containing two clauses.  Copy out your matched up sentences and underline the verbs.

**Column A**
Whilst I was waiting for the bus,
Shouting as loud as I could,
Although I was feeling hungry,

**Column B**
I hated the thought of eating a cheerleader.
A car drove past and splashed me.
I tried desperately to get his attention.

Q6    Look at the clauses in column B of Q5.  Are the following statements about them true or false?

a)  They make sense on their own.
b)  They are full sentences with a verb.
c)  They are main clauses.

Q7    Look at the clauses in column A of Q5.  Are the following statements about them true or false?

a)  They make sense on their own.
b)  They are full sentences with a verb.
c)  They are subordinate clauses.
d)  Subordinate clauses are often marked off from the main clause with a comma.

Q8    Pair up a clause from column A and a clause from column B to produce three full sentences:

**Column A**
If I revise,
If I went to the party,
If we had practised,

**Column B**
I would enjoy it.
I will do well.
We would have won.

# Specialist Vocabulary / Jargon

*Sometimes people baffle you with a whole load of words you don't understand — often to do with a particular job or subject. These words are called **jargon**, or just **specialist vocabulary**.*

**Q1** Match up the following sets of jargon words with the correct occupations — don't worry if you don't understand all the words:

> Medical jargon (language of doctors, nurses, hospitals)
>
> Legal jargon (language of lawyers, law and solicitors)
>
> ICT jargon (language of IT workers, network administrators, computers)
>
> Education jargon (to do with school, teachers and students)

> prosecution, *habeus corpus*, witness, contempt of court
>
> levels, attainment targets, assessment, objectives, SEN
>
> cardiac arrest, fracture, defibrillator, contusion, hypertension
>
> router, TCP/IP, device driver, bad cluster, interface

**Q2** Individual school subjects have their own specialist vocabulary too. Match up the sets of specialised words to the correct school subject:

| Art Science PE | agility, tactic, mesomorph, recovery, choreographic, deltoid muscle<br>abstract, surreal, frieze, impasto, spectrum, kiln<br>combustion, condensation, method, freeze, photosynthesis |
| --- | --- |

**Q3** Write down six jargon words to do with each of these subjects:

a) Mathematics
b) Music
c) Design and Technology

**Q4** Choose one word from each list of six in Q3 and explain it in your own words.

**Q5** Write down whether you think each of these statements is true or false, and give a reason in each case:

a) Using and understanding jargon words can improve your understanding of a subject.

b) Specialist vocabulary helps when you need to explain something specifically or precisely

c) Not knowing jargon words in a particular subject can leave you feeling confused or left out.

d) Using specialist terms correctly in your writing, in all your school subjects, from Science to Music, will get you really good marks and / or a pat on the head from your teacher.

## Bottle still here — but jar, gone...

You're supposed to write well in <u>all your school subjects</u>. So, <u>learn</u> all that <u>specialised vocab</u>.

# Connectives

**Q1**  Match up the following definitions of sentence types with the correct terms from the box.

a) Two or more ideas joined together with 'and', 'but' or 'or'.

b) A sentence with two or more ideas not joined with 'and', 'but' or 'or' (often the ideas are linked with other words and / or commas.)

c) A sentence with one idea.

> simple sentence
>
> compound sentence
>
> complex sentence

**Q2**  How many ideas are there in each of the following sentences?

a) Rajwant had to run in order to catch his plane.

b) Rajwant had to run so that he would catch his plane.

c) Rajwant had to run, as he had to catch his plane.

d) Rajwant had to run to catch his plane.

e) Rajwant had to run because he needed to catch his plane.

f) Rajwant had to run so as to catch his plane.

**Q3**  Are the sentences a) to f) in Q2, compound, complex or simple sentences?  Give a reason.

**Q4**  What is the **reason** for Rajwant running?

**Q5**  Copy out the sentences in Q2 and circle the words which **introduce** the reason for Rajwant to run.

> In English jargon, these words are called "connectives that express <u>purpose</u>". They're all alternative ways of saying that one thing is because of another.

*Ideas about **expressing a reservation** (e.g. a concern, doubt or a worry about something) can be added onto a sentence.  They form a **subordinate clause** of a **complex sentence**.*

**Q6**  Copy out these sentences and circle the words that **introduce** the idea of a reservation, concern or doubt:

> You're looking for words that introduce the <u>subordinate clause</u>. Remember that the subordinate clause doesn't make sense on its own.

a) She went out running, although she guessed it might rain.

b) Tim paid the restaurant bill for the meal, despite having a poorly paid job.

c) Anthony was determined to get fit, even if it meant giving up his favourite ice cream.

d) Mrs. Smith would stop Claire's pocket money, if it was the only way to make her study!

**Q7**  Re-write a), b) and c) of Q6 with the subordinate clause at the beginning.

**Q8**  Is it a good plan to write some sentences with the subordinate clause at the beginning, and some with it at the end?  What does this add to your writing?

# Phone a hotel quickly — express your reservation...

Learn different ways of saying "because" or "but".  It'll make your writing dead sophisticated — and it'll stop your reader getting bored, cos you won't be writing "because" and "but" all the time.

# Figurative Language

**Q1**    Say whether you think these phrases are meant **literally**, or not:

     a)   "The team's got many rivers to cross before they can get to the final."

     b)   "My leg is killing me."

     c)   "They treat me like a slave around here."

     d)   "They don't pay me very well, and they give me too much work."

**Q2**    Match up the correct meanings to each of these terms:

     a)   **literal** language        i)   Means **exactly** what it says.

     b)   **figurative** language    ii)   Gives you a picture or an idea that's related to what it means.

**Q3**    Which of these two meanings of "The team's got many rivers to cross before they can get to the final" do you think is correct? Which describes the **literal** meaning, and which describes the **figurative** meaning?

     a)   In order to reach the final the team will physically have to cross a lot of rivers, by bridge, by boat, or by swimming across.

     b)   The team has a lot of challenges to overcome before they can get to the final.

**Q4**    Say whether each of the following things refers to the **literal** or **figurative** meanings of "**many rivers to cross**":

     a)   wetsuit            e)   inflatable raft

     b)   courage           f)   dedication

     c)   swimming certificate    g)   determination

     d)   practice           h)   bridge

**Q5**    Use **figurative** language to write **two different sentences** expressing each of the following ideas. Your two sentences for each idea should have a different **feel** to them.

     a)   I'm hungry.              c)   The hamster died.

     b)   Jim lives in a remote village.    d)   Megan and Phil have broken up.

**Q6**    What can figurative language do in a piece of writing to make it better to read?

**Q7**    Why is it a good idea to use figurative language in your creative writing?

**Q8**    Why is it a bad idea to use figurative language in your scientific writing?

# Language Choice

**Q1**   Give an example of how each of the following would affect the words you'd choose to use:

a)   whether you're speaking or writing

b)   who you're talking or writing to

c)   what you're talking or writing about

**Q2**   Look at this list of people.  Who would make you think **really** carefully about your word choice?  Why would you think so carefully about the words you chose?

a)   friend?

b)   teacher?

c)   parent?

d)   headteacher?

e)   police officer?

f)   server in a coffee bar?

**Q3**   Look at this list of written tasks.  Which ones would make you think a lot about your word choice?  Why?  What might happen if you didn't choose the right kinds of words?

a)   shopping list?

b)   e-mail to a friend?

c)   final assessed project for school?

d)   letter to your teacher about relaxing the rules on school uniform?

*When we think about word choice we're making a decision based on whether a situation is **formal** or **informal**.*

**Q4**   Finish the sentences a) and b) with the right definitions:

a)   Formal language is...

b)   Informal language is...

...relaxed, friendly language with everyday casual word choices.

...making careful word choices based on the expectations of the conversation or written task.

**Q5**   Which of the following situations would require formal language and which would be best in informal language?

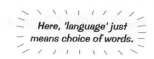
*Here, 'language' just means choice of words.*

a)   talking to a large group of people

b)   talking about a serious topic or explaining a difficult topic

c)   talking or writing to people we know well

d)   talking or writing to people we don't know well

e)   talking or writing quickly about a very familiar subject

# Language Change / New Words

Q1   New words replace old words.  Which of these statements explain why this happens?

a)   Words are sometimes like clothes — they just go out of fashion and new ones replace them.

b)   Older words get replaced with new words that are easier to say or are abbreviated (made shorter).

c)   New inventions have never existed before.  Obviously, a new 'thing' needs a new name — just like a new baby needs a name.

d)   A writer in a dictionary office decides to make up some new words for a laugh.

Q2   Why do you think **ICT** (information communication technology) has so much **specialist vocabulary**, and so much **new** vocabulary associated with it?

Q3   What does the 'e' stand for in 'e-mail'?

Q4   What is the abbreviated form of 'World Wide Web'?

Q5   Finish off this sentence.  The word 'web' is a good word choice in the phrase 'World Wide Web' because a web has lots of strands that...

Q6   Research the following words.  Answer the questions after each one.

a)   Internet — what is it?  Why "net"?

b)   Dotcom business — what does that mean?  What does dotcom refer to?

c)   website — what is it?  Why "web"?  Why "site"?

d)   search engine — what is it?

e)   download — what does it mean?  "Down" from where?

f)   online — what does it mean?

g)   router — what is it?  What does a router actually route?

h)   ISP (Internet service provider) — what does an ISP do?

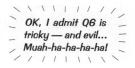
*OK, I admit Q6 is tricky — and evil... Muah-ha-ha-ha-ha!*

Q7   The online / internet world is known as **"cyberspace"**.  What do you think someone who spends a lot of time on the Internet might be talking about when they refer to **"meatspace"**?

Q8   Think of as many other words associated with electronic communication as you can (at least 15).  Now make a dictionary aimed at people over the age of 70 who have minimal knowledge about computers and the Internet — you'll need to explain as clearly as you can!

## ICT and when ICT I drinks it...
*This joke also features in a CGP Science Workbook. Hey — you just can't keep a great gag down...*

It's one thing to understand all the ICT jargon — it's another to say <u>why</u> it means what it does.

# Implications and Irony

*Choice of words can mean the difference between telling the truth or... not quite telling the truth. Sometimes the writer's real feelings are hidden behind the literal meaning of the words.*

**Q1** Copy out the sentence and circle the four words in the sentence that suggest that Edith is probably the only one who thinks her clothes are hip.

> **Wearing her hippest gear, or so Edith thought, she headed to the party.**

*The writer isn't saying straight out that Edith is probably the only one who thinks her clothes are hip. Instead, the writer has used words that **imply** a deeper meaning (so you have to look for, and figure out, the hidden meaning or **implication** of the words). When word meanings are not obvious, this is also known as being **implicit**.*

**Q2** The **opposite** of being implicit is to make your meaning really clear and obvious, so the reader puts the minimal effort into working out what you mean. What's this known as?

a) being boring

b) being explicit

c) using words of one syllable only

***Punctuation** around a word can often be a writer's technique of actually saying the opposite.*

**Q3** Read the sentence below, then copy out and finish off this explanation: The word 'ill' actually means the opposite, because Steve was not ill, he just didn't want to...

> **Oh, so Steve was off school because he was genuinely 'ill' with a serious case of spelling test phobia?**

**Q4** A writer or speaker can write or say the opposite of what they actually mean. When you say something about someone and you actually mean the opposite, this is called:

a) irony or being ironic

b) being nasty

c) a white lie

**Q5** Write down implicit versions of the following explicit statements. Use quotation marks, hidden meanings and irony.

a) Marvin is usually very late to meetings.

b) Fiona's mum is a slow driver.

c) I think what you just said was rubbish, and it contributed nothing to the conversation.

d) Sharilyn spends most evenings in because she doesn't have a lot of friends.

# Yeah, right — I really "enjoyed" writing this page...
You need to figure out when people mean the opposite of what they're writing — you do, honest.

# Combining Clauses

*Sentences can be divided up into distinct parts called **clauses**.*
*Every clause has at least one verb.*

**Q1** The following sentences have two clauses.
Copy them out and add a comma to separate the clauses.

*Hint — just stick the comma in the most obvious-looking place.*

a) I'll tidy up my room if I can ever find the time.

b) There was a lull in the fighting so I ran like mad for cover.

c) There was never a dull moment when my aunty was behind the wheel.

d) What chance was there of survival given that all the life jackets were missing?

e) You know that dinner is ready when the microwave explodes into flames.

**Q2** Commas can be used to join clauses together to form a sentence.
Complete each of these sentences by adding an appropriate clause after the comma:

a) In the event of an emergency,

b) While the teacher's back was turned,

c) There would never be a better opportunity to go on holiday,

d) My mind always plays tricks on me,

e) During the course of only five minutes,

**Q3** The following is a list of what are called non-finite clauses.
Use each of them to write a sentence. They don't have to be used at the start.

a) there is no doubt in my mind
b) who would have thought
c) having said that
d) in retrospect
e) as a matter of course
f) in no way
g) as expected
h) to be precise
i) putting myself in their shoes
j) is beyond doubt

## I dreamt there was a hideous, hairy sentence — with nasty, big clause...

If you chopped a sentence up in the obvious places, you'd end up with <u>clauses</u>. They're usually joined together with <u>commas</u>. And don't forget, grammar-spotters, every clause needs a <u>verb</u>.

# Choosing Your Words

**Q1**  When making a statement it is best to get straight to the point.
Write a short and direct sentence about each of these subjects:

  a)  fox hunting
  b)  James Bond movies
  c)  secondary school
  d)  your best friend
  e)  Christmas Day
  f)  nightmares

**Q2**  When writing about subjects in depth, your sentences need to be more detailed.
Expand upon these short sentences by adding a few more details about each subject:

  a)  The apple was green.
  b)  My foot was sore.
  c)  My uncle is rich.
  d)  The soup was foul.
  e)  This inmate is dangerous.
  f)  The ride was exciting.

**Q3**  Write **either** a short **or** a detailed sentence for the following examples.
For each one, explain why your choice of sentence is appropriate.

  a)  An advertising slogan for perfume.
  b)  An advert for a hotel in a holiday brochure.
  c)  A film poster quote for the latest Hollywood blockbuster film.
  d)  Instructions on how to operate a fire extinguisher.
  e)  The description of a film in a film guide.

**Q4**  The following argument isn't effective because lots of the sentences are too short and jump from one point to another.  Rewrite the sentences to make the argument more convincing.

> *"I didn't do it.  I was framed.  I was watching a television programme about how leopards will drag their prey into the branches of trees to keep them from other predators.  I heard a loud noise.  It made me jump.  I called the police.  While I was waiting for them, I had a large ham sandwich with pickle, mustard and lots of ketchup.  As they knocked on my door, I saw my husband's legs hanging over the balustrade.  They were covered in blood.  I screamed.  The police broke the door down and arrested me.  I didn't do it.  I was framed."*

## I've lost my goat... Has anyone seen my goat?  Doris... where are you?

There's no point in advertising a chocolate bar in 100 words or writing an essay in 10 — think about what you're writing it for and then decide.  *It would* be great if essays only needed to be 10 words long...  If only...

# Proper Punctuation

*Good use of punctuation makes your sentences easier to read.*

Q1 Copy out these sentences and replace the full stops
with **either** a question mark **or** an exclamation mark:

> Doris! Doris!
> Where are you?

- a) How can you say that.  They ate his brains.
- b) Is this legal.  Where is the emergency stop button.
- c) That is a dead hamster.  What is the meaning of this.
- d) When can I go home.  Look out, it's the police.

Q2 Speech marks identify the person who is talking.  Write a sentence for each
of these characters, remembering to use speech marks in the right place:

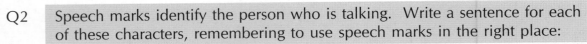

> **e.g.  A tennis umpire to a player — "The ball was in," said the umpire to the player.**

- a) A policeman arresting a suspect.
- b) An actress accepting an award.
- c) A teacher scolding a pupil.
- d) A general giving an order.
- e) A gardener talking to his roses.
- f) A vicar preaching to his congregation.
- g) A politician addressing Parliament.
- h) A palm reader telling a fortune.
- i) A madman screaming at a lamppost.

*Colons can be used to add extra information to a sentence
(often to explain the first bit of the sentence, or give examples).*

Q3 The colons in the following sentences are in the wrong places.
Write out the sentences and put the colons back where they should be.

- a) "I'll tell you something else: you don't know that I hate rice pudding."
- b) Paul often gets confused last week: he spread shoe polish on his toast and
shined his shoes with butter.
- c) "I'll tell you how: the other team beat us so easily they cheated from start to finish."
- d) The brain surgeon had something: much more important on his mind his hot
date with the nurse from reception.

*Semicolons can be used to introduce contrasting statements.*

Q4 Complete each of these sentences by adding a contrasting statement after the semicolon:

> **e.g.  Adventure can be exciting; routine is awfully dull.**

- a) Good English lessons are interesting;
- b) Facing challenges can improve character;
- c) The basking shark is a gentle giant;
- d) I like to spend time with my friends;
- e) Regular exercise is good for you;

## Punctuation is great fun, there's no denying that...

Punctuation might not be very exciting, but it's important to use it properly if you want your
sentences to make sense.  Just think if there were no full stops, you'd go on and on and on and...

# Changing Your Tenses

*The word 'tense' refers to **when** things take place: in the **past**, **present** or **future**.*

**Q1** Put each of these sentences into the past tense:

a) "I can't talk now; I'm driving in the motorway fast lane at ninety miles per hour."
b) "This is the most exciting World Cup game I've ever seen."
c) "The suspect is now leaving the building via the underground car park."
d) "I'm finding it hard to breathe and I can't concentrate properly."
e) "Where is the light switch? The room is in total darkness."

*Changing the tense from **past** to **present** can make
things seem more real — as if they're happening now.*

**Q2** Rewrite these sentences by putting them into the present tense:

**e.g. I'd hurt myself badly ⟹ "I'm in a lot of pain right now."**

a) I didn't know what was happening.
b) We had found her mobile phone in the cloakroom.
c) I had walked all day and night.
d) The game finished hours ago.
e) I was having a lovely holiday.
f) She'd been unhappy for a while.
g) I loved her.
h) The explosion had destroyed everything.
i) The lesson was really boring.

"He's just so tense..."

**Q3** The sentences below have been changed from the present to the future tense.
Fill in the gaps with the correct words from the box. You can use them more than once.

| going | be | to | will | shall |
|-------|-----|-----|------|-------|

**e.g. I like this. ⟹ I will like this.**

a) Your mum is waiting for you there. — Your mum ........ ........ waiting for you there.
b) This is working. — This ........ work.
c) We are having afternoon tea with the Queen. — We ........ have afternoon tea with the Queen.
d) I am working in the supermarket. — I am ........ ........ work in the supermarket.
e) The atmosphere is amazing. — The atmosphere ........ ........ amazing.

**Q4** Write out a sentence for each of the following subjects.
One should be in the past tense, one in the present, and one in the future.

a) Watching a film at the cinema.
b) Being ill with flu.
c) Eating an expensive meal.

## I'm present — you can't changed me. But I already had, won't I?

Here's another fun page for you. Tenses are pretty useful because they tell the reader <u>when</u> things are happening. It's important to use the right one and not <u>mix them up</u>.

# Making Conditions

*Conditional clauses* usually contain *'if'* and say what **might** happen in given circumstances.

**Q1** Copy out these conditional clauses and add on appropriate endings:

*e.g.* **If you had been paying attention, you might have found out where the cheese is.**

a)    If you had been paying attention,
b)    If this problem isn't addressed immediately,
c)    If I don't think of something quickly,
d)    If we'd locked the pig pen properly last night,
e)    If this were all you had to offer,

*When remembering how to use conditional clauses, it is useful to think of them as 'nagging' clauses.*

*Modal verbs* are often used to say what **might** happen.

**Q2** Write a sentence using each of the following modal verbs:

*e.g.* **might — If I have enough money, I might be able to go.**

| | | | | | |
|---|---|---|---|---|---|
| a) | can | d) | may | g) | could |
| b) | shall | e) | will | h) | would |
| c) | won't | f) | should | i) | must |

*Modal verbs* are also useful for talking about a hypothesis.

**Q3** Write a sentence or two giving your response to each of the following hypotheses. Try to use the words from Q2 in your sentences.

a)    Giving free bananas out in school will reduce truancy.
*e.g.* **Giving free bananas out in school might reduce truancy if the bananas had magic powers.**
b)    Blondes have more fun.
c)    Being wealthy is more important than being happy.
d)    You can tell a person's character from their appearance.
e)    Taller people command more respect.

**Q4** Rewrite the following non-conditional paragraph by making it conditional. I've started it off for you.

*e.g.* **I went on holiday to California ➡ If I were to go on holiday, I would go to California.**

*I went on holiday to California. The weather was so hot and sunny that it was a crime not to spend a lot of time sunbathing on the beach. I did so many exciting things. But swimming with sharks has to be the best. It was the best holiday I've ever had.*

# *Producing Paragraphs*

*The 'chronology' of events is the order in which they took place.*

**Q1** Paragraphs need to describe a sequence of events clearly.
Make sense of this paragraph by rearranging the sentences into the right order:

> *We entered the bank at twelve o' clock midday and forced everyone to lie on the ground. We disguised ourselves as nuns, to conceal our true identities. We put the money into bags under our robes and exited the building calmly, one by one. Dave D. Dangerous blew open the main vault, using his special mix of nitroglycerine and alcohol. We watched the bank closely for a week, getting to know the security guard's routine.*

*Sentences which make **comparisons** can be linked together to form well-developed paragraphs.*

**Q2** For each of these examples, write a short paragraph which compares and contrasts the two subjects:

a)   television and reading

b)   cinema and theatre

c)   cartoons and comics

d)   term time and holidays

e)   cities and countryside

**Q3** You can give a paragraph a clear focus by including examples which illustrate your point.
Write down a list of examples which could be useful when discussing each of these subjects:

a)   smoking

b)   the effects of tourism on the Lake District

c)   terrorism

d)   the benefits of watching television

e)   big game hunting

**Q4** Write a paragraph about a subject of your choice.
Make sure you use each of the methods on this page.

## *Poor Jim jumped out of a plane and tried to open his paragraph...*

There's more to writing than just waffling about your opinions. You've got to order your points logically and give reasons to back them up — for example, say <u>why</u> you like Gareth more than Will...

# Bringing Paragraphs Together

*The **subject** of one paragraph should lead on directly to the next
so that the paragraphs are linked together.*

Q1 For each example, write a sentence which explains the connection between the two subjects.

    a) A footballer and a referee.
    b) A teacher and their pupils.
    c) A car driver and their passengers.
    d) A film director and an actress.
    e) A microwave and a dishwasher.

***Recalling** what was said in the previous paragraph
makes the link between two paragraphs more obvious.*

Q2 Say which of the sentences below follow on effectively from a
paragraph about the underlined subject. Answer 'yes' or 'no'.

    ***e.g. <u>Fishing</u> — We have seen how catching freshwater trout can be a challenge. (yes)***

    a) <u>stamp collecting</u> — As stated previously, my cousin had an awful memory.
    b) <u>gardening</u> — Now we know how to plant a rosebed, we can move on to
       making the border.
    c) <u>wrestling</u> — It has to be repeated that this woman was absolutely gorgeous.
    d) <u>sprinting</u> — It may be presumed then, that he'd never boiled onions in his entire life.
    e) <u>writing</u> — Having talked about joining sentences into paragraphs, it seems
       appropriate now to discuss the linking up of paragraphs themselves.

Q3 The following 'linking phrases' can be used to show a connection between paragraphs.
For each one, write two sentences which use the linking phrase to connect two ideas together.

    a) In addition to this
    ***e.g. Cyril wanted to take over the world. <u>In addition to this</u>, he hoped to invent a gerbil-scrubber***
    b) There can be no doubt
    c) Is it any wonder then
    d) With hindsight
    e) It should be noted
    f) To state the obvious
    g) Moving on from there
    h) Putting it a different way

Q4 Write two paragraphs on a subject of your choice.
Make sure you link them together using the methods on this page.

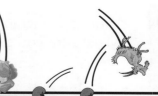

# Cilla brings paragraphs together on (wait for it) Blind Punctuate...

So just remember, your paragraphs should lead on from each other. Ouch. OK, who threw that?
Come back here, you little twerp. I'll get you. How <u>DARE YOU</u> say my Blind Date joke wasn't funny.

# Subjects and Styles

**Q1** Each academic subject requires a particular style of writing. Examine the style and vocabulary of these sentences and write down which subjects they belong to:

a) We can see that the population growth in Kenya is well above the regional average.

b) The evidence would suggest that Napoleon lost the Battle of Waterloo due to bad strategy.

c) The experiment had proved that punching someone with a brick will make them unconscious.

d) Calculate the correct answers by solving the equations.

e) Drill two-centimetre holes into the steel block at fixed intervals of five centimetres.

*Scientific language and style need to be precise and exact.*

**Q2** Imagine your own experiment and write a sentence for each of these headings in a scientific manner:

a) Equipment

b) Predictions

c) Observations

d) Results

e) Conclusions

Results of experiment...
I appear to have grown a tail...

*Historical analysis must make convincing arguments because it is open to interpretation.*

**Q3** Write a criticism of this pupil's historical account of the 1991 Gulf War, suggesting how their style, vocabulary and grammar might be improved:

> The Gulf War started on Tuesday, when I had the mumps and it was in Kuwait which is very hot and expensive. It was America versus Iraq who had big moustaches and thought they could rob Kuwait's oil. George Bush was the American Boss and he was right angry with Iraq for being nasty to Kuwait so he sent clever bombs down their chimneys to teach them a lesson. Mum says we helped too because we're best friends with them. Anyway, we won easy and Iraq have still got big moustaches but they are a bit greyer now.

**Q4** Write a historical analysis of a recent event at your school, following your own advice about style, vocabulary and grammar given in Q3.

## Science, bah — can it prove why I hate bananas?...

You have to be precise when you're a scientist. But I'm not sure I really agree with that, I mean it's sort of, almost, maybe rubbish — no?

# Pleasing the Crowd

*The style and presentation of a text should always depend on who you're writing for and what you're trying to do.*

Q1   Come up with an advertising slogan for each of these products:

a)   a sports car

b)   an acne treatment

c)   a luxury sofa

d)   a silent dishwasher

e)   cheap novelty jewellery

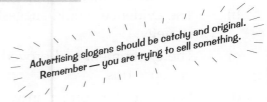

*Advertising slogans should be catchy and original. Remember — you are trying to sell something.*

*Presenting information well is essential. You might have something really important to say, but no one will listen unless you can make it interesting.*

Q2   Make a list of all the points you'd want to make in a documentary about each of the following. Explain how you would present each in an interesting way.

a)   road traffic accidents outside school

b)   cosmetic plastic surgery

c)   skateboarding

d)   bullying in school

*Editorials present your personal views to others in the hope they may share them.*

Q3   Write an editorial to persuade your classmates that they should be doing **either** more **or** less homework.

Q4   Decide whether an advertisement, a documentary or an editorial would be most appropriate for each of these subjects, and then explain your choice of styles:

a)   the cost of sports footwear

b)   non-stick frying pans

c)   football hooligans

Q5   Write a newspaper article about something that happened recently at your school. It should include the following:

a)   an eye-catching headline

b)   opening paragraph with: **what** happened, **where**, **when** and **who** was involved

c)   details of what happened

d)   people's opinions (usually in the form of quotes from interviews)

e)   conclusion (this is your chance to give your own opinion)

## *I never please the crowd — I have hygiene issues...*

It's a good idea to think about who's going to read what you've written. I'm not saying that you have to be a suck-up or anything, just think about what stuff your reader might like. Like cheese.

# Being Formal with the Text

*Informal text often uses the **first person** (I, we, our etc.), while formal text is much more likely to use the **third person** (they, them, he, she etc.), often in the **past tense**.*

**Q1**  a)  Say whether the following sentences are written in the first person or the third person.

   i)   I am not an ogre.
   ii)  She wasn't sure how to juggle.
   iii) We wanted to go sailing.
   iv)  They are almost dwarves.

   b)  Say whether each of the sentences from part a) is written in the past or the present tense.

**Q2**  These sentences have been written in the first person.
Rewrite them in the third person (either male or female) and in the past tense.

   *e.g. "I can't see a thing." — She could not see anything.*

   a)  "We're under attack!"
   b)  "I am very sorry."
   c)  "Our hands are tied."
   d)  "I trust Jack completely."

> an **active** verb is when someone/something does the action,
> *e.g. they ate the biscuit*
> a **passive** verb is when the action is done to someone/something,
> *e.g. the biscuit was eaten by them*
> passive verbs are more formal.

**Q3**  Alter the style of these sentences from informal to formal, by changing all the active verbs into passive ones:

   *e.g. I am talking to you. — We are talking together.*

   a)  Anna wrote the poem.
   b)  He saw you.
   c)  An evil little elf bit me.
   d)  The teacher caught us.

**Q4**  The following passage has been written informally. Use all of the techniques you have studied on this page to rewrite it in a formal style.

> I was hurrying along the corridor feeling anxious, when I saw her moving quickly towards me. I started panicking and began running up the stairs, desperately trying to avoid her. Following as fast as she could, she screamed "please wait!" Stopping to face her, I heard her continue, "you've been dodging me for too long." Looking straight into her eyes I replied, "I'm sorry but I have nothing to say to you." I passed her, and was crying openly as I walked back down the stairs. Behind me, I heard her sigh quietly, "I will never speak to you again."

# Standard English and Dialect

*Standard English is the formal way of expressing yourself.*
*Dialect is your own way of talking in your part of the country.*

**Q1**     Say which of the following expressions are in
standard English and which are in a regional dialect:

a)     I wish to make a complaint about the quality of the cockles sold in this establishment.

b)     I'm really fed up to the back teeth with this blooming horrible fizzy pop.

c)     Shut it, will you?  Can't you see I'm trying to sleep?

d)     The attacking footballer showed incredible dexterity on the pitch; he deserves to be well paid for his services.

e)     Please children, do keep the noise down and show some respect for your elders.

f)     That striker played a blinder today; he's worth every penny he's paid.

**Q2**     In which of the following situations is it advisable to use standard English?

a)     writing to apply for an astronaut's training course

b)     shouting to a friend to pass you the ball in the yard

c)     showing visitors around your school

d)     writing a letter of complaint to the Prime Minister
about the amount of homework Year 8 pupils have to do

e)     giving a foreign tourist clear directions (in English) to the motorway from your house

f)     arguing over which video to watch at your friend's house at the weekend

**Q3**     Change the following examples of dialect into
standard English (I've done the first one for you):

a)     Your mam's going to play merry hell with you for the state of your shoes.
       ***Answer:  a) Your mother will be cross with you for the state of your shoes.***

b)     I'll have three glasses of pop, and give us two bags of them beetroot flavoured crisps.

c)     The criminal said he'd not nicked the motor nor nothing else but the judge didn't believe a dicky bird and he sends him to do porridge for five years.

d)     This Vincent van Gogh geezer was a right famous painter what got so upset with his girlfriend that he only went and sliced his own ear off, didn't he?

**Q4**     Which of the following are rules for standard English?  Write TRUE or FALSE for each one.

a)     You should use full words such as 'I am' in place of abbreviations like 'I'm'.

b)     You should use polite vocabulary and avoid colloquial words, such as 'wagging it' when you mean 'playing truant'.

c)     Verbs and subjects should agree (e.g. 'We was late' is dialect and the standard English version is 'We were late').

d)     Soap operas provide a good example of correct spoken standard English.

## Eeee by gum I knows not what tears thar splunge...
Quite right — splunge is vital.  Just remember not to swear at your teachers.  Not out loud, anyway.

# How to Be Formal and Informal

Q1   Say which of the following types of text are formal and which are informal:

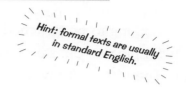

- a)   head teacher's prize day speech
- b)   e-mail to a friend
- c)   application for an important job
- d)   school science report
- e)   text message to a friend
- f)   school history essay
- g)   teenager's diary
- h)   encyclopaedia entry
- i)   newspaper report of invasion by aliens from Mars

*Hint: formal texts are usually in standard English.*

Q2   Choose two examples from Q1 (one formal and one informal) and write a paragraph for each.

*Choosing whether to write formally or informally depends on **who** you're writing for and **what** the circumstances are.*

Q3   Below is a list of people and circumstances.  For each one, choose one of the levels of formality shown in the box.

| very formal    quite formal    fairly informal    very informal |

- a)   writing a letter of apology to your head teacher
- b)   holiday postcard to your best mate
- c)   an advert for an anti-spot cream for teenage magazine readers
- d)   text message about a football match to your best mate
- e)   information about Shakespeare to be read aloud to your friends in class

Q4   Write out the full text for examples a, b, c and d given in Q3.

*The passage below comes from Isobel's diary.  She wrote it after having been late for school. Unfortuately, her head teacher wants a written explanation for why she was late.*

Q5   Write a formal version of the passage that Isobel can hand in to her head teacher.

Dear Diary,
It all started when I had to drop our Alex off at her school
and it was tipping it down with rain and so we both got soaked.  So I thought to myself that I might as well go home and get changed rather than go to school all miserable and wet, but of course by then the bus had gone, making me walk and that's when I met the ten-foot killer (aka the Head Teacher) at the gate.  She is a right moody old ratbag.  And her breath smells.

*hint: take out some of the 'ands'*

## My grandmother dresses formally — what of it?...

My grandmother speaks very formally.  I find that throwing in the odd bit of cockney rhyming slang usually shakes her up.  "Wotcha grandma — 'ows about a trip down the apples and pears?"

# _Ways in Which Words Have Changed_

Q1    Which of these sentences were written by Shakespeare and which are modern?

   a)  It's a revolutionary breakthrough in technology: no wires, no electric circuits, nothing to be switched on or connected.

   b)  So please you, step inside.

   c)  Thou knows't my daughter's of a pretty age?

   d)  Peace, peace, Mercutio, peace!  Thou talkst of nothing!

   e)  Simon Shepherd is one of the most prodigiously gifted forwards to wear the white shirt of England.

   f)  Thou liest, thou shag-hair'd villain!

   g)  Ah me, what news, why dost thou wring thy hands?

   h)  You have the bedside manner of a rattlesnake.

> When Shakespeare was writing his plays (1564 to 1616) people really did say <u>thee</u> and <u>thou</u> instead of _you_, and <u>thy</u> instead of _your_.

Q2    Copy out the following quotations from Shakespeare, replacing the 'thou' or 'thee' bits with modern English.  (I've underlined some of the other bits that also sound out of date — replace these with modern words too, if you can.)

   a)  "Shall I compare thee to a summer's day?  Thou <u>art</u> more lovely and more <u>temperate</u>."

   b)  "<u>Turn thee</u>, Benvolio, and look upon thy death."

   c)  "Thou villain, Capulet!"  → you probably can't rewrite the word villain without swearing, so we'll leave this one as it is...

   d)  "<u>Else would I</u> very shortly see thee there:"

   e)  "Why <u>dost</u> thou smile <u>so</u>, and kiss thy hand so <u>oft</u>?"

   _hint: temperate means (roughly) calm and stable_

Q3    Now rewrite the sci-fi dialogue below so that the modern bits sound Shakespearean.

   _Hint: replace <u>you</u> and <u>your</u>, <u>are</u> and <u>do</u>.  That should get you going..._

> **Dr Vibe's assistant:** _You are dead lucky, Doctor.  That titanium plate in your bonce deflected the laser blast away from the dead centre of your tremendously powerful but devious brain._
>
> **Dr Vibe:** _What do you mean, you cringing assistant?  What are you saying?_
>
> **Dr Vibe's cringing assistant:** _I mean to say that your life is no longer under threat.  And the foul Professor Pertang will never endanger your plans again._
>
> **Dr Vibe:** _Yippee! Pass me your pack of powerful peppermints.  I feel like celebrating.  In fact, cringing assistant, you can give the cat a mint too._

Q4    Say which of the following statements about Shakespearean language are true and which are false:

   a)    People said 'thee' and 'thou'.

   b)    Sentence structures were <u>exactly</u> the same then as they are today.

   c)    Verbs sometimes ended in **-st** (e.g. "dost" and "didst").

   d)    Other verbs sometimes ended in **-th** instead of **-s** (e.g. "loveth" instead of "loves").

   e)    There is <u>no</u> Shakesperean vocabulary which a modern reader can understand.

# English and Other Languages

**Q1** The English language has absorbed many words from the people who have invaded England over the centuries. Match each French word below to the English word that derives from it:

a) Le porc
b) Le veau
c) Le boeuf
d) Le beurre
e) La fleur

veal
pork
butter
flower
beef

**Q2** *Mark's German penfriend has written him the following letter, and has asked Mark for help with his English.*

Dear Mark

I to you am for your help asking. I much better with my English want to get. Please my writing study and then to me a reply send. I would very much my writing of English sentences like to improve. You will write back to me soon with your suggestions, yes? Did you Man United match on the television watch?
Love Jan

a) Write Mark's corrected version of the letter.

b) What do you think is the main difference between German and English sentence structure?

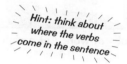

*Hint: think about where the verbs come in the sentence*

**Q3** *Trish has a french penfriend. Colette has written to Trish asking for her help.*

Dear Trish

I hope you go well. Thank you very much for your letter; I found her on the doormat when got home from school. School — I do not like her so much at the moment. I am having to read an English book at the moment — I find him very difficult and I do not like him! But I love your English pop music! I have just bought a new CD by The X-Ray Mutant Radio Gang — she is an excellent disc!
Love Colette

a) Write Trish's corrected version of Colette's letter.

b) Point out the main difference between the gender of English and French nouns.

**Q4** The following English food words are derived from either French or Italian. Say which country each word comes from.

a) lasagne
b) croissant
c) pizza
d) meringue
e) minestrone
f) baguette

# Combining Information from Sources

*We often have to take information from more than one source, and combine them into one piece of writing.*

*Learning how to 'read' sources properly can really speed things up.*

Q1    *Here are three sources about dating:*

**Source 1** — *a bar graph*

We asked 100 people in their thirties how each of them met their partner.

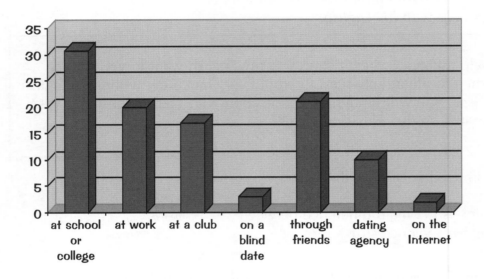

**Source 2** — *an interview with a male aged 31*

"I met my wife in my workplace. I wasn't expecting it. She just walked in one day as a new staff member and I fell for her right there on the spot! Love at first sight."

**Source 3** — *excerpt from an advertising leaflet for a dating agency*

'In today's busy lifestyle, so few of us get the opportunity to relax and meet single members of the opposite sex. We take the strain out of meeting compatible others, so you can get the partner you deserve.'

Read the above sources and use them to write a paragraph describing the different ways people meet their partners. Be sure to include information from each source.

## Take your partner by the hand — no not like THAT...

"When my baby left me, I found a new place to dwell. It was down at the end of lonely street. That's Heartbreak Hotel now baby. You make me so lonely baby, you make me so lonely baby, oh you make me so lonely, I could dieeeeahhhieeee... uh-huh. yeah baby. OOOOOh yeah baby..."

# Using Reading Strategies

*Even good readers sometimes need to 'guess' what words mean.*

*Look at these two texts about a sports event:*

**Source 1** — *news report* — *sports pages of 'The Herald', June 2318*

> Into the arena walked the railstrom ready to do their best.
> They held the fredus in their hands tightly, ready for the
> opposition to begin their turn bowling. The horses of 'United'
> charged and the whizzbits hurtled toward the goal of our national
> side, but Neil held firm in goal. His performance was match-winning,
> the hour was tense and yet only one time-out was required for poor
> sportsmanship. Well done our boys!

**Source 2** — *TV interview with Mike Neil, June 2318*

| | |
|---|---|
| Interviewer | Well done Mike, a real blinder! |
| Neil | Thanks, they kept coming, but we held them off. It was a railstrom effort, not just me. |
| Interviewer | It has to give us a real chance tomorrow. |
| Neil | Absolutely, we only had one whizzbit get through, I can't believe our Riders won't do better than that tomorrow. |

**Q1** Describe what you feel a **whizzbit** and a **fredu** are. (You will probably have to read back carefully and work out the meanings of words you don't know.)

**Q2** How do you think this futuristic game would be played? As you write this answer, refer to the sources as you use them — so acknowledging them.

**Q3** The word **railstrom** was used twice. Does this help you work out what it means? Say what you think it means, giving your reasoning.

**Q4** **RESEARCH** — *Try to find your own report about a game you know very little about. You could try looking in the sports section of any newspaper — or go for something a little more challenging.*

> **e.g. the rules of croquet or mah-jong.**

What words in the report are new to you? How do you use your knowledge of language to help you make sense of something that may otherwise be very complicated?

# Making Notes in Different Ways

*There are many ways you can make notes.  Much of what we see or read is unnecessary information and can be cut out.*

Q1    Say which of the following are ways of taking notes:

i)    drawing diagrams (star charts etc.)

ii)   writing bullet points from a video

iii)  abbreviating for speed and ease of retrieval

iv)   all of the above

*Read this interview with an 'eyewitness' to a crime:*

---

Interview with Simon Sneve, aged 24

Int    Simon, what happened?

SS    Well, it was Friday and I'd had a busy day paying a few bills.  Then I'd been to the hairdressers for a new 'Beckham' cut.  I think I'd then picked up 'The Sun' for a read at the park, as it was such a lovely day.

Int    Okay, so you were in the park relaxing and reading the paper.  What next?

SS    An old red car pulled up outside the bank.  It was making a bit of a din as I think its silencer had gone.  There were two masked men inside, and they got out and ran really quickly into the bank. They were carrying rifles, but I've no idea if they were real or not.  I heard some screaming and then the bank alarm went off.  A strange thing happened next as this young red-headed girl just wanders over to their car and lets down their back tyres!!

Int    That was brave!

SS    I suppose it was.  But anyway, what happens next is that the robbers run out of the bank carrying two plastic bags full of 'swag'.  But as they get in the car, they start it up and get no further.  By the time they get out to look, the police have arrived and are arresting them.

Int    Was it exciting?

SS    Well, it all happened very fast.  I suppose it was all over in less than five minutes.  But, yes it was exciting.  I've never seen that sort of thing before.

Int    Thank you for the interview.

---

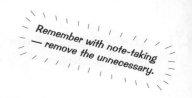

*Remember with note-taking — remove the unnecessary.*

Q2    What information here is essential for you to know what happened?  Write down the three most important facts.

Q3    Present the 'scene' as three cartoon-style pictures with speech bubbles as appropriate.

Q4    Look at some similar texts.  Do other interviews contain large amounts of 'waffle'?  Why do you think the needless information still gets printed?

# Developing Ideas and Themes

*A text or speech often develops ideas, themes or values.*

*Have a careful look at this letter sent to the local council:*

Dear Sir / Madam,

As a local resident of Dale Park housing estate, I wish to complain about the lack of facilities for the young.

Every night youths gather outside my house and, as my house is an end of terrace building, they use my back wall for kicking balls against. They also play loud music on stereos and ride bikes up and down the pavements. This causes me upset as I need to relax after a hard day at work.

The behaviour of the youths is not aggressive, but they are obviously bored and I get used to endlessly having to pick up litter each morning — which also upsets me.

Whenever I have asked the young people why they are always here, they point out that, apart from the bus shelter, there is nowhere else to go. There is an obvious need for a hall or playing area here.

Please, as a council, can something be done as regards facilities?

Thank you.

Q1   This begins as a letter of complaint, but is complaining the only theme of the letter?

Q2   What do you feel the writer of this letter feels to be most important — helping the young, or moving them away from his / her house? Why do you think this?

Q3   What are the main ideas of the letter?

Q4   Do you feel any sympathy for the writer? What solutions might help everyone?

## Buses are like, er, buses — you wait for, er, um, d'oh...

Why do old people ALWAYS complain about YOUNG people? I blame it on the television. They watch far too much of it. That's where the grannies get all their ideas from you know. TV is bad...

# Recognising Bias and Objectivity

*There is always bias in history. History tends to be written by the 'winners', or at least by one side. Inconvenient facts might be left out, and opinions might be stated as facts.*

*Look at these three sources about Richard III:*

**Source 1** — *interview with a modern 'supporter' of the king*

"Richard now has his own society. We believe he is innocent of the crimes attributed to him by Shakespeare and others. We enjoy dressing up in medieval clothes and listening to the music of the times. He was a great king and would have led us into a new age if he hadn't lost at Bosworth."

**Source 2** — *quote from* Richard III *by William Shakespeare (act 1, scene 1), with commentary*

"I am determined to prove a villain,
and hate the idle pleasures of the days.
Plots have I laid, inductions dangerous,
By drunken prophecies, libels, dreams …"

*In the play, written some one hundred years after the death of Richard III, Shakespeare creates a murderous villain who destroys his entire family in order to get the throne. It is a great story, but Shakespeare was a storyteller who worked for the Tudors — the family who defeated Richard.*

**Source 3** — *historical entry submitted for a reference book*

Richard III (1483-1485) married Anne Neville. One son Edward (d. 1484) and an illegitimate daughter Kathryn. As king he toured the country. Defeated at the Battle of Bosworth 1485.

Q1    List the **facts** contained in each source.

Q2    What **opinion** of Richard III do we get from each of the sources?

Q3    List the sources in order of objectivity, starting with the most biased and ending with the least biased. Explain your answer.

Q4    Which, if any, of these sources are helpful to a historian? Why?

Q5    Is it possible to write 'the truth' now about someone who lived so long ago? Explain your answer.

## Didn't I tell you not to trust anyone... *(evil cackling begins)* ha... ha ha ha...

You need to <u>watch out</u> for bias — it's quite tricky to spot. You need to keep asking yourself "is this fact or just someone's onion?" Got it? (Did I say onion again? I meant <u>opinion</u> — I'm *always* doing that...)

# Implied Meanings in a Text

*Sometimes when we read a text we have to identify some meaning 'beneath' the text, an implied meaning that may take the form of **irony** or **satire** or just good old fashioned **sarcasm**.*

---

**Sarcasm** — *sarcasm is the name for any language that makes fun of something. It's normally ironic, but it doesn't have to be. Sarcasm's all about the tone of voice.*

---

**Q1** Say which of the following sentences are sarcastic and which are not:

a) "So nice of you to join us." *(said to someone walking into a lesson late at 9.20 a.m.)*

b) "Oh, well done." *(said to a child who spills a can of coke over their work)*

c) "The Duke died at 10 'o'clock this morning." *(said by a radio presenter)*

d) "Pay that footballer more — at £80 000 a week how can he manage to feed his family?" *(said by a radio presenter)*

e) "There's enough cake for everyone." *(said by a mother at a birthday party)*

---

**Irony** — *An ironic remark can be one that <u>says</u> one thing, but <u>means</u> something else (often the opposite).* **e.g. "I really think that footballer deserves £80,000 a week."** *This could be said sarcastically, but it's <u>more</u> than plain old sarcasm.*

---

*You can have ironic situations too — ones that have two elements that seem strange when they happen together — e.g. catching a cold after having a flu injection. Complicated, isn't it?*

**This is not irony.**

**Q2** Say which of the following is an ironic situation, and which is not:

a) having a driving instructor crash into your car

b) a woman, who is afraid of children, being a schoolteacher

c) buying a dog and then taking it for a walk

d) eating ice cream with your fingers

e) next door deciding to have a noisy party on the one night you go to bed early

---

**Satire** — *Satire is a bit more formal — it's when you put together a criticism of someone's bad points (usually in a book, a poem, a play, or even a stand-up comedy routine). Satire uses sarcasm, irony and other types of humour. There is an example below:*

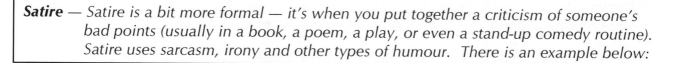

*"Queen Pandora — your people love you and you are respected by all," said the servant.*
*"I know," said Queen Pandora.*
*"Will you be eating your usual helping of boiled babies this evening?" asked the servant.*
*"I certainly shall," said Queen Pandora, "and I'd like them cooked medium-rare this time."*
*The servant sighed happily and walked away, proud to be serving such a wonderful queen.*

---

**Q3** Write your own short example of a piece of satire. If you're stuck for ideas, why not write about someone you know, or someone else famous (e.g. David Beckham, Sara Cox)?

# _Changing Meanings_

Q1   Read the following bit of text and decide what is going on.  Choose from the options below:

"I'm just not sure how I feel
about this fruitcake — I'm
not sure I should eat it,"
said Bob.

   i)   Bob is uncertain about eating the fruitcake.
   ii)  Bob hates the fruitcake, but is trying to be polite.
   iii)  Bob loves the fruitcake and is being ironic.
   iv)  Bob is upset because the fruitcake makes him think about cheating on his girlfriend.
   v)   There is no way to tell because we aren't told how Bob says his line.

Q2   Say how you might be able to tell what the line really
means, if it was presented in each of these forms:

   a)  a radio play
   b)  a TV documentary
   c)  a glitzy Californian soap opera
   d)  a photo to accompany the text

Q3   _Look at this passage taken from_ Oliver Twist _by Charles Dickens:_

The girl had taken a few restless turns to and fro — closely watched meanwhile by
her hidden observer — when the heavy bell of St Paul's tolled for the death of another
day.  Midnight had come upon the crowded city.  The palace, the night-cellar, the jail,
the mad-house; the chambers of birth and death, of health and sickness; the rigid face
of the corpse and the calm sleep of the child — midnight was upon them all.

Decide how you would make this written description visual if you
were making a film of the story.  You could think about the following:

   a)  camera angles
   b)  lighting
   c)  cutaways
   d)  location
   e)  costume
   f)  casting

Q4   Now, looking at the passage again, think about how you could use sound to add
to the atmosphere — this could be sound effects, background music, or both.

# Technology to Tell Tales

**Q1** Match the quotes from the stories below to the appropriate sound effect from the box.

| baby crying | | birds singing |
|---|---|---|
| | police siren | |
| heavy traffic | | |
| | | thunderstorm |

a) "I can't wait to get away to somewhere clean and unpolluted."

b) "Mwa ha ha ha ha! I have you now — there can be no escape! You will be my vampire bride... forever!"

c) "I just can't look after these kids any longer!"

d) "This is the best move we've ever made."

e) "I don't feel safe here anymore — there's too much crime."

**Q2** Copy these bits of dialogue and suggest sound effects in brackets to add to the meaning.

a) (............) "This school is driving me mad."
b) (............) "Yes. Yes. I will marry you."
c) (............) "We'll never get out of here alive."
d) (............) "Row, you miserable creatures. Row!"
e) (............) "I need those figures on my desk first thing tomorrow morning."

**Q3** Imagine you are a computer game designer. Your heroine is trapped in an underground cave system. Write three sound effects you could use.

**Q4** Now decide on the physical characteristics of your heroine — she needn't be human.
(You can cut out pictures from a magazine or newspaper, use a computer, draw her or describe her.)

**Q5** Explain why your heroine should look like your choice, and what audience you would aim your computer game at.

**"There ain't no sharks in here"** *(cue shark music)* *(cue "aargh...")* *(cue crunching sound)*

Spielberg definitely knew what he was doing with the 'Jaws' music — no messing about. Couldn't have done it with whale noises though. Just a load of high-pitched squeaks. Not scary at all...

# **Structure**

Q1    The examples below (a to f) are all introductions (or openings).
Say which type of text each one is, choosing from the box.

a)    I can't remember being born.  You may think this is quite a normal thing to forget, but I put it down to a terrible lapse in my memory, probably brought on by my disgust at what was happening to me at the time.

b)    It was noon.  I usually get up around now and wait for the phone to start ringing.  Thieves, muggers or murderers — they're all the same to me, and I ain't scared of any of 'em.

c)    A young healthy child, well nursed, is at a year old a most delicious, nourishing and wholesome food, whether stewed, roasted, baked or boiled.

d)    In the year 927 King Athelstan did drive out King Gulfrith.

e)    A cloud went by, along the coast.
I felt my pulse to see
If I could count my heart beats out
and time them by the sea.

f)    My Aunt had urged me to visit the old castle.  When I saw the battlements shrouded in mist, a sharp sense of forboding awakened deep within my heart.

| | Lyric Poetry | |
|---|---|---|
| Historical Chronicle | | |
| | Autobiography (real or fictional) | |
| | Gothic Horror | |
| Satire | | Crime Fiction |

Q2    *Read the following extracts (they're quite similar):*

**A**    *Kieron had thought the ghost walk would be fun.  When he'd bought the tickets, he'd been expecting to be amazed by tales of crazed demons and axe-wielding maniacs.  In fact, all that happened was that he and his girlfriend Jane were bored to tears, trudging through freezing cold snow, following the tour guide.  They slipped away from the crowd and went into the nearest shop to warm up.  This decision would change both of their lives forever, on account of the mysterious stranger who was waiting for them inside.*

**B**    *Kieron had thought the ghost walk would be fun.  He'd been expecting to be amazed by tales of axe-wielding maniacs, not to be bored to tears trudging through freezing cold snow.  He and Jane eventually slipped away from the crowd, and went into the nearest shop to warm up.  "Well that's that then," said Jane, "I guess there aren't any ghosts here after all."  They both sighed, and stared out of the window in silence.*

a)    One of these is an **introduction** to a story and one is a **conclusion**.  Say which is which.

b)    How can you tell which is the introduction and which is the conclusion?

## *If I had a goat for every time someone's said that...*

I'd be, well, swimming in goats.  Not very practical really.  Although you can make cheese out of them.  Well, out of their milk.  Making cheese out of a fully live goat would be quite silly really...

# <u>Themes</u>

*Read the following extracts.*
*I've underlined some of the most important bits.*

**A**

Thou wast not born for death, <u>immortal</u> Bird!
No hungry generations tread thee down;

**B**

At once a voice arose among
    The bleak twigs overhead
In a full-hearted evensong
    Of <u>joy illimited</u>;
An <u>aged</u> thrush, frail, gaunt, and small,
    In blast-beruffled plume,
Had chosen thus to fling his soul
    Upon the growing gloom.

**C**

Open here I flung the shutter, when, with many a flirt and flutter
In there stepped a <u>stately</u> raven of the saintly days of yore.
<u>Not the least obesiance made he</u>; not a minute stopped or stayed he;
But, with mien of lord or lady, perched above my chamber door —"

*obesiance = a show of respect or politeness (e.g. bowing to someone)*

*mien = appearance*

**D**

(The old man has been talking to a small bird that has landed on his boat. He's thinking about all the little birds he's seen get eaten by hawks.)
    But he said nothing of this to the bird who could not understand him anyway and <u>who would learn about the hawks soon enough</u>.
    "Take a good rest, small bird," he said. "Then go in and <u>take your chance</u> like any man or bird or fish."

*go in = to the shore*

**Q1**     What theme runs through every one of these extracts?

**Q2**     Say which of the following statements are true, and which are false:

*who came first?*

a)     Extract A seems to celebrate the existence of birds.

b)     The bird in extract B sings very joyfully.

c)     The bird in extract B is young and spritely.

d)     The bird in extract C seems very polite.

e)     The man seems wiser than the bird in extract D.

f)     In extract D, birds are told to behave like fish.

g)     In extract D, the man advises the little bird to be brave and face life.

**Q3**     Choose any one of these extracts and write a paragraph explaining how the bird is represented in it.

# Emotional Responses

*Read the following extracts.  They're all about sailors.*

A

> Once again I stood at the water's edge, and as
> I gazed out to sea, I felt as if I were being rocked
> in the arms of a great beast, mighty but gentle.
> No ship was in sight, but my heart ached a little less.

B

> I ran up the cabin stairs as the storm howled around
> us. "Cut the rope, Jack!" yelled the skipper.
> "We don't get that sail down right now, we're done for."
> I stumbled towards the fo'c'sle, but my groping hand
> couldn't find the knife I always carried in my pocket.

C

> Little thinks he that has a happy life on land.
> How I, miserable, clutch anxious minutes
> At the mercy of the waves.  On the whale-road,
> Hail fell in showers, coldest of grains.

Q1    a)    What do you think the writer of extract A feels about sailing?

b)    What do you think the writer of extract B feels about sailing?

c)    What do you think the writer of extract C feels about sailing?

Q2    List the words that each writer uses to describe the sea and the weather around them.

Q3    Which extract do you like the best?  Explain why.

Q4    Write the next paragraph of extract B, so that the story is concluded.

*Hint — remember to keep the tension up and make it dramatic, so it fits in with the first part.*

# We are sailing, we are sailing — and I'm vomiting...

It's all very well to learn all the technical stuff, but what you really want is to be able to read something and say "I like it because..." or "I hate it because...".  Take this tip for example. It's making me feel rather ill.  And I'm the one writing it.  Euch...

# Recognising the Form

Q1    Copy the sentences below and fill in the blanks from the word list in the box.

a)    A sonnet has ............ lines, divided into an octet and a sestet, or three ............ and a couplet.

b)    A Gothic novel usually features a ghost or a ............ .

c)    A romantic comedy usually ends ............ .

d)    Political satires often ............ someone's appearance, mannerisms or ideas in order to make us laugh at them.

e)    A ballad is a ............ poem which can be set to music.

f)    Tragedies normally end ............ .

| | | | |
|---|---|---|---|
| narrative | happily | quatrains (4 line verses) | exaggerate |
| fourteen | in tears | | monster |

*Interviewers should use formal language, unlike normal conversation.*

Q2    Rewrite the following conversation so that it sounds more like an interview for a restaurant job.

**Owner**:    Hey — so you like food?
**Applicant**:    Sure.
**Owner**:    You think you might like working in this joint?
**Applicant**:    Why not?
**Owner**:    You think you'd be okay with serving stuff to people all day?
**Applicant**:    Yeah — I never get sleepy.
**Owner**:    I like your style baby — you're in.
**Applicant**:    Hey, cool.

Q3    See if you can use the linguistic clues in the texts to match the following extracts with a genre and time period from the box below:

a)    Harold, his kinsman, recovered his body and conveyed it to Winchester, where he was buried beside Cnut, his uncle. The king and the whole army declared Sveyn to be nithing (*without honour*). Eight ships he had before he murdered Beorn: afterwards all forsook him except two.

b)    And did the Countenance Divine
Shine forth upon our clouded hills?
And was Jerusalem builded here
Among these dark Satanic mills?

c)    "What happened, man?"
"After you passed out, I poured some vodka over the wound. You kinda jumped, you know, but you didn't wake up."
I tried to turn over on the bed, but the pain was like a razor, slicing my mind as well as my shoulder. What had Big Joe done with the gun?

d)    "But," said Elizabeth, "Queen Victoria now has Gladstone as her prime minister, and he, at least, *does* care about the women walking the street because they can find no other work."

| | | | | |
|---|---|---|---|---|
| i) | 20th-century American crime fiction | | iii) | 19th-century realist novel |
| ii) | 11th-century historical chronicle | | iv) | early 19th-century poem |

# Response to Other Literary Texts

*Read the following extract from* Moby Dick *by Herman Melville:*

> *"But what takes thee a-whaling? I want to know that before I think of shipping ye."*
>
> *"Well, sir, I want to see what whaling is. I want to see the world."*
>
> *"Want to see what whaling is, eh? Have ye clapped eye on Captain Ahab?"*
>
> *"Who is Captain Ahab, sir?"*
>
> *"Aya, aye, I thought so. Captain Ahab is the Captain of this ship."*
>
> *"I am mistaken then. I thought I was speaking to the Captain himself."*
>
> *"Thou art speaking to Captain Peleg — that's who ye are speaking to, young man. It belongs to me and Captain Bildad to see the Pequod fitted out for the voyage, and supplied with all her needs, including crew. We are part owners and agents. But, as I was going to say, if thou wantest to know what whaling is, as thou tellest ye do, I can put ye in a way of finding it out before ye bind yourself to it, past backing out. Clap eye on Captain Ahab, young man, and thou wilt find that he has only one leg."*
>
> *"What do you mean, sir? Was the other one lost by a whale?"*
>
> *"Lost by a whale! Young man, come nearer to me: it was devoured, chewed up, crunched by the monstrousest parmacetty that ever chipped a boat! — ah, ah!"*

Q1  a)    Ishmael is the name of the unidentified sailor.
          What is the name of the captain he is talking to?

    b)    What type of boat is it?  Choose from one of the following:

          i)    fishing boat
          ii)   whaling boat
          iii)  cross-channel ferry

    c)    What is the name of the boat?

    d)    What happened to Ahab's missing leg?

*Read this next extract, taken from* Fathers and Sons *by Ivan Sergeyevich Turgenev:*

> The scenery which the party were traversing could not have been called picturesque, for, with slight undulations, only fields, fields, and again fields, stretched to the very horizon. True, a few patches of copse were visible, but the ditches, with their borderings of low, sparse brushwood, recalled the antique land-measurement of many years ago. Also, streams ran pent between abruptly sloping banks, hamlets with dwarfed huts (of which the blackened roofs were, for the most part, cracked in half) stood cheek by jowl with crazy grinding-byres of plaited willow, empty threshing floors had their gates sagging, and from churches of wood or of brick which stood amid dilapidated graveyards the stucco was peeling, and the crosses were threatening at any moment to fall.

Q2  a)    Which of the following best describes the landscape:

          i)    hilly and cold
          ii)   fairly flat and boring
          iii)  full of lakes

    b)    Are the houses in the hamlets they travel through
          in good condition?  Say how you know.

    c)    Use your own words to describe the condition of the churches and graveyards.

# Planning Your Work

*All work needs to be carefully **planned**. This allows you to structure your work into **clear paragraphs**.*

**Q1**   Copy out the following story plan in the correct order:

a)   The wolf shows himself and tries to eat Red Riding Hood.

b)   Red Riding Hood goes through the woods, meets the wolf and tells him where she's going.

c)   When Red Riding Hood arrives at her grandma's house she notices Grandma's strange appearance.

d)   They all live happily ever after.

e)   The woodcutter hears Red Riding Hood shouting for help. He kills the wolf and rescues Grandma.

f)   The wolf goes to Grandma's house. He locks Grandma in the cupboard and disguises himself by wearing Grandma's nightclothes.

g)   Red Riding Hood's mother sends her to take groceries to her grandma, but warns her to ignore strangers, especially the wolf.

*Writing follows a particular format. We don't start with 'and they all lived happily ever after', as we know that comes at the end. By writing a plan we can ensure we cover **everything** we want to say — in the **order** we want it in. This works for any type of writing.*

**Q2**   An editor has asked you to write a news report about what happened to Red Riding Hood. List everything you want to include in your report (try to keep to around 7 or 8 points).

*Now you need to decide on the **order** of your article. Remember that with a news article the reporter often starts with a summary of the story.*

**Q3**   Using the list you wrote for Q2, number the points in your list to show the order you have chosen for your report.

**Q4**   Now write your article, following the schedule below.
Don't spend more than five minutes on each point in your list.

a)   Write a paragraph about the first point on your list. Time yourself to ensure you don't take longer than five minutes.

b)   Now reread your first paragraph. Are you happy with it? If not, change it.

c)   Once you are happy, move on to the next point in your list...

d)   Repeat until you have covered everything on the list.

**Q5**   Reread your completed article. Are you happy with it?
If not, change the bits you dislike to complete your article.

---

## Decide the order: chicken burger, fries and a strawberry milkshake...

**Remember: Planning your writing** (munch) **ensures you don't forget to** (slurp) **include anything. Make each** (munch munch) **point in your plan into a new paragraph to give it structure.** (Mmm, this *is* a tasty burger...)

# Thinking About the Reader

*By rereading what you've already written you can make it better. Rather than just saying* **what** *happened, describe* **when**, **where**, **how** *and* **why** *it happened.*

**Q1** Read the following sentences. Think how they could be improved and then write the redrafted version. The first has been done for you.

a) John was scared as he walked down the corridor.
*John trembled as he peered into the darkness. Bravely he took a step into the narrow passageway, breathing heavily. The sound of his heart pounding in his ears was deafening as, stumbling over the uneven surface, John started down into Hell.*

b) The creature moved and Harry jumped in surprise.

c) The graveyard was quiet and creepy.

d) Michael looked down at the broken toy and cried.

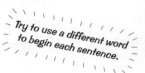
*Try to use a different word to begin each sentence.*

**Q2** Rereading our work also allows us to change the style. Write down what **style** each of these sentences is written in (e.g. legal document, newspaper report, poem, fairy story, etc.).

a) Yesterday a man was found murdered in his flat. Police investigations are under way, but as yet the motive is unclear.

b) Once upon a time there lived a lonely girl called Cinderella.

c) Under subsection c, paragraph 2, it is declared that on no occasion can the guarantee be transferred.

d) Dear Amy, Thanks for your letter. I just wrote to say what a great time I had when I came to stay last week.

e) Poems often rhyme,
If you have time,
But this line doesn't.

*Remember, the <u>style</u> of a piece of work is extremely important and will have an <u>effect</u> on the reader, making them feel a particular way.*

**Q3** Choose **two** of the above styles of writing (e.g. letter and poem) and write the following statements in those styles. I've done an example of a final draft for you.

**Statement**
The bank was robbed at 3.30pm. The culprits were six men in balaclavas. £10,000 was stolen.

**As a poem**
£10,000 stolen,
From the bank
On the corner.
3.30pm it happened.
6 men, faces covered.
They ran.
It's gone.

**As a letter**
Dear John,
    You'll never believe what happened yesterday — the bank was robbed! They got away with ten grand.

**Q4** Now write each of the following statements in **two** styles of your choice:

a) The schoolboy was on his way to school when he was knocked over by a car driven by a 17-year-old boy who was drunk.

b) The school was set on fire by local youths. They were arrested and detained at a youth custody centre.

c) Michael ran to the suitcase and flung it open. It was full of gold and jewels.

# Recording Ideas to Help You Solve a Problem

**Q1**     The council has been given a grant to pay for improvements in your area.
Assuming there's nothing for young people to do, answer these:

    a)    Write down three things you like to do in your spare time.

    b)    Write down three things that would improve your area.

    c)    Choose your favourite idea from part b) and write down three advantages of the council implementing your idea.

    d)    Write down three disadvantages of the council implementing your idea.

    e)    Who would benefit from your idea?

    f)    Who would it affect in a negative way?

**Q2**     Write a proposal to say why your idea from Q1 part c) should be chosen.  Follow the letter plan below:

---

Dear Mr Smith,

    I think we should use the regeneration grant to...
*[describe your idea and say what you would need to do to implement it]*

    The people who would benefit from this are...
*[use notes from e) above and try to think of as many people as you can and why it is a good idea]*

    Some people who could be inconvenienced are...
*[use your notes from f) and as well as saying who would be inconvenienced, say how you could make it easier for them]*

    Looking at the advantages, I believe...
*[say here all the good things about your idea (use notes from c)) — make people want to choose your idea above all others]*

    However, I have also considered the negative viewpoint and some people may believe...
*[say here some of the disadvantages (use notes from d)), but remember to say how they could be overcome]*

    Overall I believe this is the best proposal because...
*[finish by saying what the effect on the community would be, and why this is the best idea of all]*

    Yours sincerely,
*[write your name here]*

---

**Q3**     Check through your letter for errors.  Then make sure you have used all of your notes.  Then, if necessary, write a final draft of your letter.

---

## So CLEARLY, the best option for everyone is to give it ALL to me...

This page is good practice in thinking about <u>different sides</u> of an argument — which you have to do <u>all the time</u> in English.  So for example, you'd need to think about the <u>downsides</u> of knocking down a few blocks of houses to build the world's biggest tiddlywinks arena, as well as the obvious benefits.

*Section Nine — Essay Skills*

# Developing Fluent, Legible Handwriting

*Most days of your life you will write something, whether it is a shopping list, an essay or a card. Your handwriting needs to be **legible** (easily read). You also need to be able to write quickly (especially in exams).*

Q1    Print the alphabet in lower case (not capitals) like this:

*To print means lifting your pen after each letter — you are not joining the letters.*

abcdefghijklmnopqrstuvwxyz

*Now imagine that there are two lines drawn across the alphabet you've printed, like this:*

abcdefghijklmnopqrstuvwxyz

*Notice how **b**, **d**, **f**, **h**, **k**, **l** and **t** are tall letters and go above the line. The letters **f**, **g**, **j**, **p**, **q** and **y** all have tails below the second line. All the other letters fit in between the two lines.*

Q2    Now print the alphabet in upper case (capitals) like this:

ABCDEFGHIJKLMNOPQRSTUVWXYZ

*All of these letters should reach above your imaginary lines.*

Q3    Now write the following sentence in joined handwriting. Take your time to make it as neat as possible. Exactly the same rules are needed as when printing your letters: **b**, **d**, **f**, **h**, **k**, **l** and **t** have tops above the top line and **f**, **g**, **j**, **p**, **q** and **y** have bottoms below the bottom line.

**The quick brown fox jumps over the lazy dog.**

*You should only be lifting your pen after a word, or after **q** and **j**, which can't be joined.*

Q4    **Cursive** *(or joined) handwriting is much faster, giving you a big head start in the exams. You need to stick to the rules above for your writing to be read easily.*

Do the exercise below — you will need a partner.

a)    Write a paragraph as quickly as possible to introduce yourself to someone who has never met you. (Take no longer than 2 minutes.)

b)    Swap work with a partner and underline all the words you can't easily read.

c)    Does your writing follow the rules above for the types of letters used, and is it joined?

Q5    Now take 5 minutes to write the paragraph again, using joined handwriting and following the rules. Again swap with a partner and see if it's easier to read this time.

Q6    Now give yourself 2 minutes to copy the following paragraph (time yourself). Aim to write in joined handwriting, quickly but as neatly as possible.

John was lazy. Every day he waited for his mother to bring things to him. All he wanted to do was wait for the things he needed while he sat and watched television. His mother was not happy and decided to teach John a lesson.

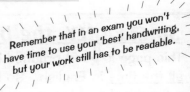

*Remember that in an exam you won't have time to use your 'best' handwriting, but your work still has to be readable.*

# Using Commentary and Description

*In English you have to use different types of **narration**. <u>First person</u> narration is where you write from your own point of view and say I, me, we, our, etc. <u>Second person</u> narration is where you address one or more people and say you, yours, etc. <u>Third person</u> narration is where you write about other people and use people's names, he, she, it, they, etc.*

**Q1**  Say whether the following sentences are written in the first, second or third person:

a)  John ran out of the room.

b)  I am so fed up with this homework.

c)  They ran away.

d)  We are so unlucky.

e)  You should pick up your book at the end of the day.

*Each type of narration makes the reader <u>feel</u> a different way.*

**Q2**  Match the following types of narration to the descriptions.

a)  **first person narration**       i)    the narrator knows everything

b)  **second person narration**      ii)   the narrator is telling us their personal version

c)  **third person narration**       iii)  the narrator is speaking to us directly

**Q3**  Read the following paragraphs and work out why the type of narration is wrong. Rewrite the paragraph in more appropriate narration. I've done the first one for you.

a)  Yasser, get Yasser a snack from the fridge. When Yasser has finished the snack put Yasser's dishes in the sink and do his homework.

> ***This is in third person narration but second person would be better:***
>
> ***a) Yasser, get yourself a snack from the fridge. When you have finished the snack put your dishes in the sink and do your homework.***

b)  Dear diary, you have had such a terrible day. First you had a terrible fight with your mum and then you were late for school.

c)  Scorpio
I have been having a bad time recently. I need to slow down and take stock of my life. Pluto in my solar house is making me feel sluggish and I should pamper myself until I feel better.

**Q4**  For each of the following types of writing, say which type of narration you think would work best:

a)  diary entries

b)  newspaper articles

c)  stories

d)  instructions you need to follow

e)  a letter explaining why your child is not able to do PE

feelin' sluggish...

# Figurative Language

Often writers will use **figurative language** to describe a character or a setting. This involves describing them as something else to make the image more powerful.

**Q1** Say which of the following sentences use figurative language:

    a)    The sea was like a wild animal, raging away at the ships until everyone drowned.

    b)    Kieron looked up at the sails longingly.

    c)    Jane flicked her hair back like a lion tossing its mane with grandeur.

    d)    Huw smelt fresher than dew on a buttercup.

    e)    Lucy got promoted and had a party.

**Q2** Turn the following dull sentences into sentences that use figurative language. Choose any image you like, just as long as it makes some sort of sense.
(I've done the first one for you, as an example.)

    a)    Jess is very successful.
       **e.g. Jess is like an ancient queen of the Nile, powerful and successful in everything she does.**

    b)    Rhiannon is very brave.

    c)    Anna is always there for others.

    d)    Alex is a pushover.

    e)    Lizzie is an angel.

**Q3**   a)    Write the name of a person in your family and write three brief descriptions of them.
          (I've done another example for you, so you get the idea...)

          **e.g.  my grandad   1. quick thinking   2. good at jumping   3. no hair**

  b)    Now write a brief figurative description for each thing you wrote down for part a).

          **e.g.  my grandad   1. like a computer   2. like a frog   3. like a bowling ball**

  c)    Now write those into one or two sentences which describe your family member using figurative language.

          **e.g. My grandad's computer brain whizzes through tricky decisions on a daily basis. He jumps like a frog, bounding around the house with his long legs, and his shiny head is like a brand new bowling ball ready to knock down a strike.**

**Q4** Now write a paragraph describing your bedroom using figurative language.

*Hint: here are some metaphors commonly used to describe rooms: bomb site, a rubbish tip, a palace.*

## My bedroom is more like a cave than a room...

Then again, I do live in the middle of deepest darkest Cumbria — we have wolves and EVERYthing.

# Thinking About Tone

*Active sentences say when somebody **does something**.*
*Passive sentences say when something **is done** (and they normally don't say who by).*

**Q1** Sort these sentences into two columns — one active and the other passive:

a) He broke the vase.

b) The vase was broken.

c) She was let down.

d) The captain stayed on the sinking ship.

e) The boat was torpedoed.

f) The house was broken into.

g) I identified the burglar.

h) He forgot to tell her the important message.

**Q2** Below are reasons for using active or passive sentences.
For each one, say which type it's talking about — active or passive:

a) when it is not important to say who did something

b) when you don't want to say who did something

c) when you want to say who did something

d) when you want your sentence to sound interesting and clear to understand

e) when you want to write something formal, like a scientific document
or a report on an event

f) when you want a detached tone

g) when you want a direct tone

**Q3** Rewrite these active sentences so that they are passive:

a) Philip broke the precious vase.

b) I carried out the experiment on Tuesday.

c) Somebody damaged the equipment.

d) A lot of people built the mosque in 1934.

e) Somebody used a fake £50 note.

f) I added carbon monoxide gas to the water sample.

g) Somebody awarded Anabel the "most beautiful baby" prize.

h) I set the old pet shop on fire.

i) The terrified pigs phoned the police.

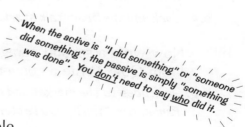
*When the active is "I did something" or "someone did something", the passive is simply "something was done". You don't need to say who did it.*

# The pig was stolen — from the flaming pet shop...

The thing about passive sentences is you don't need to say who did what — it was just <u>done</u>: the pig was held hostage at gunpoint. The kidnapper was bitten. A top tip was written about it.

# New Ways with Old Stories

**Q1**   a)    Complete the names of these traditional and incredibly dull fairy stories:

     i)       Snow ......... and the ......... .........

     ii)      Jack and the .........

     iii)     Little Red ......... .........

     iv)     ......... and the Beast

   b)    Now fill in the blanks in the same titles below, only this time use your imagination to create a really random name. (I've done the first one to give you a rough idea...)

     i)       Snow ......... and the .........

    **e.g. i) Snow White Wendy and the Monkey Forest of Panashtor**

     ii)      Jack and the .........

     iii)     Little Red .........

     iv)     ......... and the Beast

**Q2**   Choose one of the traditional fairy stories from Q1 part a). Write down some details about the story's main character, using the list below:

> ●   Name
> Age (roughly)
> Male or female
> Physical description
> Where they live (address as well as name of country)
> Personality (write three words e.g. good, kind, helpful...) ●

**Q3**   Now do the same thing for the main character of one of the stories you thought of for Q2.

*Now for the good bit — you're going to write a story involving both of these characters.*

**Q4**   a)    Start off by writing an introduction to the original fairy story from Q1 a) (make sure you introduce the character you wrote about for Q2).

    **e.g.** *Jack and the Beanstalk starts with poor Jack heading off to market to sell his cow etc...*

   b)    Now write a second paragraph, where that character meets your **new** character (from Q3). Write a conversation that they have, and say what they decide to do next.

    **e.g.** *Jack goes to the market and meets Snow White Wendy, who tells him about the Monkey Forest of Panashtor. "You'll get a better price for the cow there," she says, and they head off into the forest.*

   c)    Now make something really dramatic happen to one of the characters, then finish off your story (you could finish it so that the **other** character saves them).

    **e.g.** *Forest monkeys kidnap Jack and his cow and are going to throw them off a cliff, when Snow White Wendy reveals she has a secret magic power — she can turn monkeys into stone. She uses her magic power and saves the cow, pushes Jack off the cliff, and she and the cow live happily ever after.*

## Forest monkeys stole my mojo — not groovy baby...

I'll tell you who never lives happily ever after — the witches. They're always hungry or dead. Aww.

# Playing with Poetry

Read the following description of my dog:

> My dog George looks like he belongs on a mountain. He has thick
> wavy golden fur, and big strong paws that could climb to the moon.
> He has a big, black, shiny nose, that's always wet and curious. He's very
> stubborn, and once he starts something, he doesn't stop. You can wake
> him up with a single rustle of a biscuit packet, and you can make him
> feel guilty by stamping your foot after he's eaten a bird in the garden.

As you know, there are lots of types of poem. You're going to use the information about George to write loads of poems.

> **Free Verse**
> is where the lines can all be different
> lengths and they don't have to rhyme.

Q1 Turn the description of my dog George into a **free verse** poem.

> **A Ballad**
> has 4 lines, all the same length and same
> sort of rhythm. They have to rhyme.

*To see how they rhyme,
look at the example below.*

Q2 Use the description of George to write at least one verse of a **ballad**. You don't need to stick to the description *too much*. It's only there to give you some ideas.

Here's my verse, just to give you an idea:

My dog George is old and tall
And he looks like a mountain goat.
His fur is fair and his nose is wet
And he smells like a rancid stoat.

*the second and fourth lines
have to rhyme*

stoat?

> **A Haiku**
> is only 3 lines long. The lines have a certain
> number of syllables in them: 5, 7 and 5.

*See what a haiku looks like
in the question below.*

Q3 Use the description of my dog George to write a **haiku**. Here's mine, as an example:

George is my best friend: — *this line has to have 5 syllables*
He has a shiny black nose — *this line has to have 7 syllables*
And howls at the moon.

*this line has to have 5 syllables*

## You'd howl at the moon if you had to eat dog food...
Repeat 10 000 times: poetry is not for losers. Okay? Are we clear? I said are we clear? "Crystal."

# Sorting, Choosing, Presenting Information

Q1    The following descriptions come from an article about a new car.
Match each one to the type of feature it describes from the box.

| | | |
|---|---|---|
| safety | comfort | performance |
| bodywork features | interior features | entertainment system |

a)    top speed 144 mph; acceleration 0 to 60 in 3.2 seconds; 25 miles per gallon
b)    CD and DVD; 6-speaker system; Playstation built into back seats
c)    leather upholstery; chrome trim; computer-display dashboard; adjustable front seats
d)    alloy wheels; tinted glass; retractable headlights; remote-control locking
e)    twin airbags; immobiliser; rear-view-camera parking system
f)    air conditioning; heated seats; low engine noise

Q2    Write an article for a motoring magazine about the new car in Q1.
Your article should be six paragraphs long and use the information provided.

Q3    Here's a list of different ways of presenting information.
Match each one to the correct description in the box:

a)    heading
b)    subheading
c)    paragraphing
d)    diagram, photograph or illustration
e)    caption

i)      This is used to break up the text and draw the reader's attention to one bit of it.
ii)     This tells the reader the subject of the text, and it grabs their attention.
iii)    Pictures which link to the text and give the reader more information
        (or make it clearer).
iv)    This is written under a picture or photograph or diagram to tell you what is in it.
v)     A block or chunk of sentences grouped together under one topic.

Q4    Rewrite your article from Q2.  This time include a heading,
subheadings, and at least one diagram with a caption.

## *I HATE CARS — this must be the worst page in the whole book...*

When it comes to presenting your information, there's lots you can do to grab and then hold the
reader's attention.  Using headings and pictures helps make the information stand out.  (And I'm sorry
if you really hate cars, but there are some people out there who will really love this page.  Let them have a bit of fun, the saddos...)

# Explaining Things in Detail

**Q1** Improve this explanation by replacing the underlined words with a better word from the box:

> The computer has got a <u>thingamajig</u> which you use to type in words and numbers. The information is presented on <u>a thing like a TV screen</u>. When you are using the computer to <u>write something</u> you can get the computer to make sure you have spelled words correctly by using a <u>thing that checks the spellings and suggests changes.</u> When you're writing you can choose different <u>types of lettering</u> and you can also include <u>stuff like pictures</u>. Most important of all, you can pretend to be doing your homework and actually be playing a game at the same time — this is called <u>doing two things at once</u>.

| keyboard | fonts | monitor | word-process | graphics | multitasking | spellchecker |
|---|---|---|---|---|---|---|

**Q2** Complete this explanation with the correct words from the box below:

> Colds and flu ............... viruses. You can relieve the symptoms ............... paracetamol to lower your temperature, and by drinking lots of fluids. Most of the symptoms you get with a cold ............... of your body fighting the virus. Colds and flu ............... tiny drops which come out of your mouth and nose when you sneeze. The average person's sneeze ............... 100,000 virus cells for a distance of up to 9 metres. The fastest sneeze ............... over 100 miles per hour.

| are spread by | was recorded at | are caused by |
|---|---|---|
| will spread over | by taking | are the result |

**Q3** Write simple explanations for each of the following words. The first one has been done for you.

*e.g. A virus is a kind of germ which can make you ill if you catch it.*

a) virus  b) temperature  c) average  d) symptom  e) paracetamol

**Q4** Rewrite the explanation in Q2 using simpler language so that a young reader could understand it. You could start the explanation like this: "Colds and flu are both illnesses. You can make yourself feel better by ......"

**Q5** Improve these explanations by linking the sentences using suitable words from the box:

a) I broke the window. I was kicking the ball in the yard.
b) I put some spin on the ball. It was harder for the batsman to strike.
c) I taped the components to the side of the model. They would be held in place until the glue was dry.
d) The missile can make decisions as it flies. It is fitted with a computer.

| so that |
|---|
| because |

# Writing Descriptions

*The **way** in which you write a description depends on **who** you're writing for.*

**Q1** Match these descriptions to the most appropriate audience from the box:

a) description of a cricket match
b) description of a hotel in a holiday brochure
c) description of a new car in an advertisement
d) description of a missing cat
e) description of a new DVD player
f) description of a school's facilities

| | |
|---|---|
| i) | person who has two weeks off work |
| ii) | person who likes to read about sport |
| iii) | person interested in replacing their old video player |
| iv) | person whose old car has finally fallen to pieces |
| v) | members of the public who may have seen the cat |
| vi) | parents of school-age children |

**Q2** Some of the following descriptions are written in informal language and some in formal language. Sort them into two lists — informal and formal.

a) And that was a beautiful kick sending the ball straight down the pitch and into the goal.

b) The Sunny Sands Hotel is located three hundred metres from a safe beach with changing facilities and an amusement arcade.

c) The condition began with the patient developing green spots all over his body. The following day a green slime oozed out of his skin and steam hissed out of his ears.

d) It's a brilliant game. What you've got to do is to fight the Deadly Dragon and then you've got to see if you can pinch all the treasure and sneak back home without being splatted.

e) It's a totally wicked car with these cool flames painted all down the sides so it looks like it's totally on fire and it goes like a bomb.

*Clue: 'informal' language sounds like the way you would speak.*

**Q3** For each of these examples, decide whether you would write in a formal way (answer 'yes' or 'no'):

a) a text message to your best friend
b) a letter to a teacher who has moved to another school
c) a description of a day trip written in your diary
d) a description of the Queen Mother's funeral for a national paper
e) an e-mail to a friend describing your birthday presents

**Q4** Write **three** descriptive paragraphs, choosing some of the ideas in Q1 and Q3. Remember to write in the best way for your audience.

# Let Me Persuade You

**Q1**  The box shows two ways that you could start a sentence.  Add one of them to each of the statements below to make persuasive sentences.

> We all know that...
> Surely...

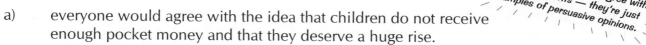
*Note: you don't have to agree with these statements — they're just examples of persuasive opinions.*

a)   everyone would agree with the idea that children do not receive enough pocket money and that they deserve a huge rise.

b)   schoolboys are much cleverer than girls, it's just that they're extremely modest and don't want to show off their intelligence in lessons.

c)   no one could disagree with the idea that the fox population is better controlled by more humane methods than hunting.

d)   modern pop music is far better and more entertaining than the boring old records our parents used to listen to when they were kids.

**Q2**  Use the sentence beginnings below to write persuasive sentences on five topics which are important to you.

a)   Certainly...
b)   We all know that...
c)   It's clear that...
d)   Surely...
e)   Obviously...

*Connecting words can be used to move straight from one point to another.*

**Q3**  Join up each pair of sentences below with the best word from the box.

> however    nevertheless    moreover    consequently    as a result

### Point 1

Whales have been hunted close to extinction.
Boys prefer PCs to books.
Bikes are cheaper than cars.
Climbing is a dangerous sport.
Uniforms make everyone look the same.

### Point 2

All hunting of whales must stop now.
There is lots to read on the Internet.
Cycling keeps you fitter.
Ropes and other equipment can make it safer.
All pupils are treated equally.

*In persuasive writing you're trying to get the reader to agree with your opinions. A good way of doing this is to use **rhetorical questions**.  These are questions which don't need an answer and can be useful in emphasising a point.*

**Q4**  Turn the following statements into rhetorical questions:

**e.g.  There's nothing wrong with loud music.  ⟹  What's wrong with loud music?**

a)   You can't watch a film without a huge tub of popcorn.
b)   You've never met a fish which complained of being hooked out of the water.
c)   You can't go to Paris and not go to the Eiffel Tower.

# <u>Making Your Arguments Clear</u>

Q1    Each statement below can be used in writing a response to one of the questions in the box. Match up the statements, i) to ix), with the question they best answer. (For each question, you should have at least one statement for and one against.)

a)    Does watching violence on TV make children more violent?
b)    Is there a serious drugs problem today?
c)    Is it right that some footballers earn more in a week than nurses do in a year?
d)    Should the cane be brought back into schools?

i)      a small proportion of violent crime is committed by youngsters
ii)     a nurse does a far more important job than a footballer
iii)    since the cane was banned, bad behaviour has increased
iv)     there has been a rise in the number of arrests for drugs-related offences
v)      this year fewer people have died from taking a drugs overdose than in previous years
vi)     footballers have very short careers
vii)    most children think it would be terrible if the cane was reintroduced
viii)   there have been several incidents of violent juvenile crime in the news recently
ix)     most children say they don't copy things they've seen on TV

*Note: these statements aren't necessarily facts. They're just examples of how you might answer the questions.*

I'm not going to set you much reading homework...

*Connectives, like the ones in the box below, can be used to emphasise the points you're making.*

Q2    Write a short answer to each of the four questions above, using only the information provided. Join up your sentences using some of the connectives from the box. I've done the first one for you.

| | | | |
|---|---|---|---|
| for example | this can be seen | in fact | in point of fact |
| in addition | furthermore | moreover | however |

*e.g. Many people think that watching violence on TV makes children violent. For example, there have been several incidents of violent juvenile crime in the news recently. However, only a small proportion of violent crime is committed by youngsters. Moreover, most children say they don't copy things they've seen on TV.*

Q3    Say which of the following phrases you might use to begin the last sentence of an argument. Answer 'yes' or 'no'.

a)    first of all          d)    finally           g)    eventually
b)    to conclude          e)    firstly           h)    in the end
c)    in conclusion        f)    in summary        i)    initially

# Good Advice

Q1 Link each of the following pairs of sentences together using the connective given. I've done the first one.

a) You could tell the truth. You could hope no one finds out.

(Or...)

*e.g. You could tell the truth. Or you could hope no one finds out.*

b) You could pay for the broken window now. You could wait until you get paid.

(Alternatively...)

c) You could go with your friend to offer support. You could wait outside the Head's room.

(On the other hand...)

d) You could wipe out the entire alien race with your laser.
You could invite them round for a pizza and a cola.

(Or...)

Q2 Turn the following instructions into advice by adding an appropriate phrase from the box. The first one has been done for you.

*e.g. I suggest that you stop smoking before it's too late.*

a) stop smoking before it's too late
b) phone a friend
c) use the phone for over three hours each evening
d) flatter your dad when you want to break some bad news

| | |
|---|---|
| i) | Why don't you... |
| ii) | Don't you think it would be a good idea to... |
| iii) | I suggest that you... |
| iv) | I advise that you don't... |

Q3 The consequences of the following sentences don't match up with the beginnings. Rearrange the sentences so that each one makes sense.

a) If you tell your brother that you took his pocket money, then eventually you're going to find it's too late and your teachers will be mad at you.
b) If you start planning the party two weeks in advance, then I will simply stop being your friend and you'll be all alone.
c) If you continually put off getting your homework done, then he will understand.
d) If you go around dressed like that, then it's not surprising that you feel a bit sick in Maths even when you can do the sums.
e) If you keep on shouting at me like that, then the guests are bound to have a great time.
f) If you eat three chocolate bars before school, then all the girls are bound to find you irresistibly attractive and Tracy in particular will fall in love with you at the Valentine Disco.

## Say NO to sad pages about cars... boycott page 60... p.60 is for LOSERS...

What's my advice for this page then? Well, you could use it to learn all about giving good advice. Alternatively, you could tear it out and make it into a little origami penguin. That's what I'd do.

# Putting the Evidence Together

**Writing tip:** *Try to include* **one main point** *or idea. Make sure you have some* **evidence** *to back it up with. Then say why this evidence proves your point — this is your* **explanation**.

Q1 Write these notes on 'Macbeth' into a full paragraph of properly punctuated sentences:

**Point:** thoughts of murder make Macbeth think he is seeing things

**Evidence:** asks himself, "Is this a dagger which I see before me?"

**Explanation:** suggests he can no longer sort out what is in his imagination and what he is really seeing

Q2 Say which is the **point**, the **evidence** and the **explanation** in these notes on 'Romeo and Juliet':

a) "She doth teach the torches to burn bright."

b) Romeo is knocked out by Juliet's incredible beauty.

c) Shakespeare compares the brilliance of Juliet's beauty to the brightness of torches to emphasise how impressed Romeo is with his new girlfriend.

Q3 Write the point, evidence and explanation from Q2 into a properly punctuated paragraph.

Q4 Write a paragraph to conclude this maths investigation using the point, evidence and explanation method of Q1 and Q3:

**Point:** boys prefer watching television, while girls prefer to read

**Evidence:** in my survey of my classmates, 86% of the boys said they preferred watching the DVD of 'Harry Potter' to reading the book, while only 33% of the girls preferred the DVD to the book.

**Explanation:** maybe boys are lazier than girls; maybe girls just don't like films; this is only a survey of my class — can't comment on whole country.

*Read this account of a fight in a lesson:*

"In Maths Craig accidentally broke Declan's ruler. At break Declan told his best mate Kevin that Craig had snapped his ruler. During English, Kevin sat next to Craig and snapped Craig's ruler so Craig punched him in the eye. Craig was sent to the head teacher for fighting."

Q5 Write down an account of the events leading up to the fight from each of the following points of view:

a) Declan

b) Kevin

c) Craig

d) Their class teacher, who has to write a balanced report for the head teacher.

*Balance means you have to take all points of view into account.*

## And so the murderer is... Professor Wigbottom [everyone gasps]

Read in a very bad French accent for full effect...

### — the false moustache gave you away. Let me explain...

You need to get in the habit of doing the "point, evidence, explanation" thing (sounds like a dance...) when you're writing essays about books. Now get-on-down and point-evidence-explanation. Oh yeah, do it baby.

# Critical Reviews

Read this magazine review of the second Harry Potter novel:

> 'Harry Potter and the Chamber of Secrets' begins at number four, Privet Drive, home of the dastardly Dursley family who so badly cramped Harry's style in Rowling's first novel.
>
> Harry Potter — in case you lot out there in reality land had forgotten — is now a wizard and in his second year at Hogwarts School of Witchcraft and Wizardry. Little does he know that this year will be as eventful as the last...
>
> The magic starts again when Ron Weasley shows up outside Harry's bedroom window one moonlit evening.
>
> I won't tell you any more in case I spoil the plot for you but — dear Playstation-addicted reader — rest assured you are in for a roller-coaster ride of fantasy, comedy and white knuckle tension. This follow-up to 'Harry Potter and the Philosopher's Stone' is just as funny, frightening and unexpected. Hogwarts School is simply a creation of genius.
>
> Be ahead of the crowd — buy it before the film comes out!

**Q1** Write down three places where the writer directly addresses their audience.

**Q2** Write down an example from the Harry Potter review for each of the following style features:

a) alliteration for emphasis   *alliteration = repetition of consonants*

b) deliberately teasing the reader

c) a simple statement of fact to convince the reader

d) a concluding instruction

**Q3** Write a 100-word review for a book, film or computer game that you've read, seen or played recently. Use the style features listed in Q2.

*The best reviewers don't use statements to say how good a book is — they use implication.*

**Q4** Say which of the following are plain statements and which are implications:

a) I had to read this horror book with every light on and the doors locked.

b) This is a really good and scary book.

c) Morris Gleitzman has produced one of the funniest novels of all time.

d) This is a really boring book and no one should be made to read it.

e) The opening of this Morris Gleitzman novel had me howling like an idiot at the predicament of Angus, the novel's reluctant hero.

f) If you cannot persuade your doctor to prescribe sleeping tablets then this book is the next best thing!

*The best reviews are entertaining in themselves and they target their reader.*

---

## "Reading CGP's book made me realise sprouts aren't so bad after all..."

Writing reviews is fantastic fun because you get a chance to really <u>rant</u> about how great or rubbish something is. Practise using the tricks from Q2 and Q4 in your reviews — you don't want to end up sounding boring when you're trying to <u>say</u> how boring something is, do you? Oh, no sirrreeee....

# The Answers

## Section One
## Spelling

### Page 1

Q1 Any correct answers. There are a lot of words in this beautiful language of ours, and not enough room in this book to write a rhyming dictionary.

Q2 a) Give my **niece** a **piece** of cake.
b) According to the **survey**, women are just as likely to wear **grey** clothes as men.
c) I **believed** it was a **thief**, and to my **relief** I was wrong.
d) Please **mail** me your price list for **sails** and surfboards.
e) We acted as soon as we **received** the letter and certainly did not intend to **deceive** anyone.
f) Don't lose **sight** of what's important - let's continue to **fight** for justice.
g) **Weighing** yourself every day won't affect your **weight**.

Q3 Local MP and bus**i**nessman wed on warmest day this summer

A local member of parl**i**ament and a well-known bus**i**nessman tied the knot in an elaborate ceremony at St George's Cathedral yesterday. The bride, whose designer dress was studded with d**i**amonds, arrived in a horse-drawn carr**i**age as temperatures soared to 30°C. The groom said he was looking forward to a long and happy marr**i**age. When asked about living with a polit**i**c**i**an, he joked, "Well, I've already got my own secret**a**ry, but maybe one day I'll have my own Secret**a**ry of State as well."

### Page 2

Q1 a) **+s** goes with ends in e
b) **+es** goes with ends in **s, x, ch,** or **sh**
c) **-f +ves** goes with ends in **f**
d) **-fe, +ves** goes with ends in **fe**
e) **-y, +ies** goes with ends in consonant **+y**
f) do nothing at all goes with e.g. sheep or deer

Q2 a) Do you ever go to the school **discos**?
b) They sold **pianos** and other musical instruments.
c) Have you brought any **photos** with you?
d) I sing alto, but Sally and Karen are **sopranos**.

Q3 a) Our hero ate (a) mango on the volcano.
b) The ship lost its / her cargo when it / she was hit by a torpedo.
c) The heavenly echo made the angel drop her / his / its halo.

Q4 a) The donkeys kicked me in the kidneys.
b) Their jerseys got stuck in the chimneys.
c) The boys found ways of mending the toys.
d) We all had ice lollies.
e) Bring your diaries with you.
f) The surveys showed what people want.

Q5 a) larvae
b) formulae / formulas
c) criteria
d) phenomena
e) bacteria

### Page 3

Q1 a) She was smiling and laughing.
b) I loved dressing up when I was little.
c) They supplied us with office furniture.
d) She looks even paler than usual.
e) We shared a drink and some crisps.
f) The weather was greyer than ever.
g) I was only joking.
h) You know I care about your happiness.

Q2 a) It's incredible that he behaved so badly.
b) Your cheek is unbelievable.
c) Your writing is only just legible.
d) The whole essay was barely readable.
e) It was terrible to see him so ill.
f) We all felt utterly miserable.
g) It's possible I made a mistake.
h) He's a very reliable chap.
i) Who's responsible for this mess?
j) There are several identifiable problems here.
k) The meal was completely inedible.
l) It was a thoroughly enjoyable evening.

Q3 a) Pay atten**tion** while I tell you which direc**tion** to go in.
b) They're demanding an explan**ation** about the accommod**ation** mix-up.
c) The team deserved that promo**tion** after putting so much energy and em**otion** into their game.
d) One brother was a poli**tician**, one was a mus**ician**, and the other was an elec**trician**.
e) The final discus**sion** was about oppre**ssion** in various countries.
f) In conclu**sion**, the state of confu**sion** which followed the

decision has not yet ended.
g) The competi**tion** hasn't finished but they're in a very good posi**tion**.

Q4 a) ends in **ant**
accountant important pleasant servant consultant relevant currant
ends in **ent**
adjacent independent ingredient component current
b) any reasonable answers
c) any reasonable answers

### Page 4

Q1 a) anti against antifreeze
b) bi two bicycle
c) contra against contradict
d) de undo/remove de-stress
e) inter between interval
f) mis wrong/bad misunderstanding
g) non not non-governmental
h) re again replay
i) sub under sub-zero

Q2 any reasonable answers

Q3 a) illogical
b) inedible
c) unbelievable
d) impossible
e) irrefutable

Q4 any reasonable answers

Q5 a) distance — television telescope telephone
b) again — replay repeat resend
c) two — bicycle bifocals bilingual
d) across — transatlantic transfer transmit translate
e) round / around — circle circulate circumstances circumference
f) listening / hearing — audience audible auditorium
g) life / living — biology biography
h) internet / computers — cybercafé cyberspace

### Page 5

Q1 a) Pass Mum's bag over.
b) Bill's football kit is filthy.
c) Ann is Elizabeth's mum.
d) Leave Jack's things alone.
e) Mrs Jackson's class is taking assembly today.

Q2 a) one sister
b) one sister
c) more than one sister
d) one sister

Q3 a) you're = you are
b) isn't = is not
c) aren't = are not
d) can't = cannot
e) it's = it is / it has
f) they're = they are

# The Answers

g) I've = I have
h) haven't = have not
i) don't = do not
j) he's = he is / he has
k) wouldn't = would not

Q4 a) **It's** a shame about the school's old guinea pig.
b) Our dog ate **its** old one.
c) **It's** got a new one now.

Q5 a) Take your things with you.
b) Give me Jane's homework.
c) Copy the work out of Tom's book.
d) The other children's parents were very nice.
e) The men's changing rooms are over there.
f) Don't forget your glasses.

## Page 6

Q1 a) "Where <u>were</u> you earlier?" said Mum.
b) "I was <u>here</u> all afternoon," said Jane.
c) "<u>Where</u> was your brother, then?" said Mum.
d) "He went to see Chrissie."
e) "<u>Who's</u> Chrissie?"
f) "She's his new girlfriend. Look — <u>there</u> they are. <u>They're</u> just coming up the drive now."
g) "<u>Whose</u> is the electric guitar?" said Mum.
h) "It's mine," said Jane. "Didn't we tell you we'd started a band? Look — Chrissie and Dan have brought <u>their</u> drum kits. Mum — where are you going?"
i) "Somewhere where I can <u>hear</u> myself think," said Mum. "Don't wait up."

Q2 a) advice
b) practice
c) licence
d) quiet
e) affect
f) quite
g) bought
h) brought
i) advise
j) practised
k) licensed
l) effect

## Page 7

Q1 Yesterday the govern<u>m</u>ent was still refusing to comment specifi<u>c</u>ally on the matter. However, a spokesman said: "The Prime Minister continues to support the Secretary of State. We have no reason to believe that he acted inappropri<u>a</u>tely in any way. Furthermore, he is an experienced and valued member of the cabinet." Supporters of the Secretary of State have reaffirmed their co<u>mm</u>it<u>m</u>ent to ensuring that he remains in office. Unfortun<u>a</u>tely, however, this issue is not likely to di<u>sapp</u>ear quickly, and observers are warning that a new strategy may be ne<u>c</u>essary. The atmosphere in Parliament yesterday afternoon was rowdy; opposition MPs called for explanations, and there were allegations of an "outrageous cover-up".

Q2 a) Let me know if I can do <u>anything</u> to help. (1 word)
b) "Thanks again for everything." "<u>Any time</u>." (2 words)
c) Does <u>anyone</u> want a game of chess? (1 word)
d) Do you want <u>any more</u> chicken?/ Do you want <u>some more</u> chicken? (2 words)
e) He doesn't play in the band <u>any more</u>. (2 words)
f) Choose <u>any one</u> card from each pile. (2 words)
g) He said <u>some things</u> that were really unkind. (2 words)
h) There's <u>someone</u> at the door. (1 word)
i) We've been dealing with this problem for <u>some time</u>. (2 words)
j) <u>Sometimes</u> you really annoy me. (1 word)

Q3 a) here — a place nearby
b) there — a place further away
c) where — used for asking questions about position or place
d) hear — what you do with your ears
e) would — used in questions such as "... you like a cup of tea?"
f) they're — they are
g) wear — what you do with clothes
h) wood — what you get from a tree

Q4 a) disappointing
b) begi<u>nn</u>ing
c) consequen<u>c</u>e
d) imaginary
e) potential
f) technology
g) streng<u>th</u>
h) persuasion
i) inter<u>r</u>upting
j) emba<u>rr</u>assed
k) ceiling
l) ma<u>rr</u>iage

Q5 any reasonable answers

## Page 8

Q1 a) They all contain "visual" or "vision". They all have something to do with seeing.
b) They all start "nutri". They all have something to do with nutrition / food.
c) They all contain "creat". They all have something to do with making or being made.
d) They all start "argu(e)". They all have something to do with arguing.
e) They all start "necess". They all have something to do with being necessary.
f) They all start "particip". They all have something to do with taking part.
g) They all contain "valu(e)". They all have something to do with value.
h) They all contain "know". They all have something to do with knowing.

Q2 any reasonable answers

Q3 a) different
b) differing / different
c) difference
d) differ

Q4 a) weakness
b) weaken
c) weaker
d) weak

Q5 a) cent
b) centurion
c) century
d) centenary

## Page 9

Q1 a) global
b) important / import / port
c) statistic
d) account / count
e) construct / reconstruct
f) callous
g) transport / sport / port
h) character

Q2 any reasonable answer

Q3 a) Does your car take petrol or diesel?
b) My pen's run out — can I borrow your biro?
c) I didn't hear the phone because I was hoovering.
d) I'll make you a sandwich for your lunch.
e) Have you got any sellotape? This page is torn.

Q4 a) NATO / Nato
b) laser
c) CD
d) BSE
e) NGO
f) quango
g) radar

# The Answers

## Page 10

**Q1** **short vowel**: hopped mopped pinned
**long vowel**: hoped moped pined

**Q2** a) Auntie Nasty pinned me against the wall and said, "You hopped around on your pogo stick right after I mopped the floor."
b) The dog pined for weeks when Pankha went to college. We hoped she would cheer up but she moped around the house for ages.

**Q3)** a) begged
b) bigger
c) stopped
d) wettest
e) tugging
f) patted

**Q4** a) Stop panicking and think.
b) I'm fed up with your constant criticism - you're always finding fault with everything.
c) He's very stoical about the decision.
d) There was a lot of tactical voting.
e) We picnicked on the grass.

## Page 11

**Q1** a) I've forgotten to double the **p** (to keep the vowel short).
b) I've forgotten to knock off the **e** before adding **ing**.
c) I've forgotten to put a **u** after **q**.
d) "dog's" is a possessive form, or a spoken form of "dog is", but it's <u>not</u> a plural form.
e) The word **full** has a double **l**. The ending **-ful** has a single **l**.
f) Most words ending in **o** just add **s** in the plural.
g) potatoes, tomatoes, mangoes, cargoes, heroes, volcanoes (etc.)

**Q2** Possible answers:
a) **Cell** is like **cellular**, **cellphone**, and **prison cell**. **Selling** is what **salesmen** do.
b) **Inter** = between, among (as in **international**, **inter-school**); **rupt** occurs in **disruptive**, **rupture**. There's an **r** on both bits of **interrupt**.
c) **conceive**, **preconceive**, **perceive**, **receive** (etc.)
d) **Dis-** is a prefix, attached to **appear**, which has a double **p**. There is also a double **p** in **reappear** and **disappearance**.

**Q3** any reasonable answers

## Page 12

**Q1** a) ne <u>cess</u> ary     ne <u>cess</u> itate
<u>inter</u> est ing     <u>inter</u> link

mis <u>cell</u> an eous    <u>cell</u> phone
embar<u>rass</u>          ass
jea <u>lous</u>             <u>lous</u> y
<u>more</u> over         further <u>more</u>
b) any reasonable answers

**Q2** a/b)
i) Sepa<u>rate</u> the <u>rat</u> from the others.
ii) They've got a <u>den</u> in the gar<u>den</u>.
iii) Ma<u>ry</u> goes to seconda<u>ry</u> school.
iv) <u>En</u>, <u>Vi</u>, <u>Ron</u> — <u>men</u> that care about the <u>environment</u>.
c) mnemonic

**Q3** any reasonable answers

## Page 13

**Q1** a) deceive receive conceive
delicious malicious capricious
ease please tease
fantastic elastic plastic drastic
come some
glove love dove
lover cover
variety piety sobriety society propriety
frustration station narration
rover Dover
tough rough enough
smother brother other mother
b) any reasonable answers

**Q2** 1 continuous jealous miscellaneous outrageous
end **-ous**
They're all adjectives / describing words.

2 boxer worker photographer lexicographer
end **-er**
They all refer to people.

3 dentist therapist linguist economist
end **-ist**
They all refer to people.

4 singing typing dancing working windsurfing
end **-ing**
They're all activities.

5 harder easier angrier friendlier redder
end **-er**
They're all comparative adjectives / describing words.

**Q3** a) resign
b) resigned
c) design
d) designer
e) photographer
f) photography
g) fantasy
h) fantasise
i) horizon
j) horizons
k) coordinate
l) ordinary
m) addition
n) additional
o) specialise
p) special

## Section Two
## Vocabulary

## Page 14

**Q1** a) iii)     b) i)
c) iv)     d) ii)

**Q2** a) iii)     b) iv)
c) i)      d) ii)

**Q3** a) ii)      b) i)
c) iv)     d) iii)

**Q4** a) iii)     b) i)
c) ii)      d) iv)

**Q5** construction
destruction
instruction

**Q6** -struct means 'build'

## Page 15

**Q1** a) true
b) false
c) true
d) true

**Q2** a) omen
b) yes

**Q3** etymology

**Q4** any four words that end in 'ly'

**Q5** c) adverb (words which describe a verb)

**Q6** a) the way Charlie paused

## Page 16

**Q1** a) *noun* — a person in charge of horses.
b) *verb* — to make a person look smart and tidy.
c) *noun* — the man who gets married at a wedding ceremony.
d) *verb* — to make a person look smart and tidy.

**Q2** By looking at what the rest of the sentence said / by looking at context

**Q3** any reasonable answers

**Q4** any reasonable answer — for example:
a) To make ends meet means to manage to have enough money to live on.

# The Answers

b) To be all heart means to be a generous, open, trusting, kind person.
c) To rake over old coals means to discuss emotionally painful things from the past.

Q5 a) true
b) true
c) true
d) false

Q6 examples — to dig up the past, to dig deep, to dig for information, to dig what someone is saying, to having a dig at someone, to dig this funky music.

## Page 17

Q1 b)

Q2 Possible answers:
a) words that name
b) words that describe nouns
c) position words, or words that relate bits of a sentence together
d) doing or being words
e) words that describe verbs

Q3 a) syntax

Q4 e) 'I like trousers.' (It's a **clause** because it has the verb 'like' in)

Q5 Whilst I was waiting for the bus, a car drove past and splashed me.
Shouting as loud as I could, I tried desperately to get his attention.
Although I was feeling hungry, I hated the thought of eating a cheerleader.

Q6 all true

Q7 a) false
b) false
c) true
d) true

Q8 If I revise, I will do well.
If I went to the party, I would enjoy it.
If we had practised, we would have won.

## Page 18

Q1 Medical: cardiac arrest, fracture, defibrillator, contusion, hypertension
Legal: prosecution, *habeus corpus*, witness, contempt of court
ICT: router, TCP/IP, device driver, bad cluster, interface
Education: levels, attainment targets, assessment, objectives, SEN

Q2 Art: abstract, surreal, frieze, impasto, spectrum, kiln
Science: combustion, condensation, method, freeze, photosynthesis
PE: agility, tactic, mesomorph, recovery, choreographic, deltoid muscle

Q3, Q4: any reasonable answers

Q5 All true. Any sensible reasons.

## Page 19

Q1 a) compound sentence
b) complex sentence
c) simple sentence

Q2 There are two ideas in each sentence.

Q3 They are complex sentences because there are two ideas in each and they are NOT joined by 'and', 'but' or 'or'.

Q4 To catch his plane.

Q5 in order to
so that
as
to
because
so as

Q6 a) although
b) despite
c) even if
d) if

Q7 a) Although she guessed it might rain, she went out running.
b) Despite having a poorly paid job, Tim paid the restaurant bill for the meal.
c) Even if it meant giving up his favourite ice cream, Anthony was determined to get fit.

Q8 Yes — it adds style and variety to writing.

## Page 20

Q1 a) to c) not literally, d) literally

Q2 a) i)
b) ii)

Q3 a) literal, b) figurative

Q4 a) literal
b) figurative
c) literal
d) figurative
e) literal
f) figurative
g) figurative
h) literal

Q5 any reasonable answer

Q6 any reasonable answers

Q7 any reasonable answers, e.g. it can create a mental picture, it gives a more interesting way of describing things

Q8 Figurative language isn't precise. It can be interpreted in different ways.

## Page 21

Q1 any reasonable answer — for example:
a) You'd be more formal when writing
b) Word choice needs to fit with who you're talking / writing to
c) Serious subjects require more serious language.

Q2 Headteacher?
Police officer?
Their authority and / or the fact that the topic of the conversation with these people is likely to be serious.

Q3 c) and d):
c) They're important, a lot depends on the results of the writing, you need to be formal when writing for teachers.
d) The teacher might think you were being cheeky with your letter or might not take it seriously.

Q4 a) making careful word choices based on the expectations of the conversation or written task.
b) relaxed, friendly language with everyday casual word choices

Q5 a) formal
b) formal
c) informal
d) formal
e) informal

## Page 22

Q1 a), b) and c)

Q2 ICT is growing quickly, and changing quickly.

Q3 electronic

Q4 www

Q5 Possible answer:
The word 'web' is a good word choice in the phrase 'World Wide Web' because a web has lots of strands that all connect together.

Q6 a) Internet — the global network of computers usually accessed by phone lines. 'Net' because it is a network.
b) Dotcom business — a company which does all its trading on the Internet. Dotcom refers to the last part of an Internet company address — .com

# *The Answers*

c) Website — A collection of files on the Internet which any other computer on the Internet can view via a browser. Web because it's on the www, and site because it's like a place which can be visited.
d) Search engine — a computer program accessed through pages on the Internet which searches through websites to help you find the site that you want.
e) Download — to take a file from an Internet site and save it to a personal computer so that it is not necessary to log on in order to access the information in the files. "Down" from the Internet to your PC.
f) Online — being connected to the Internet (e.g. via a telephone line).
g) Router — a large computer that acts as a 'node' on the Internet and makes sure requests and files get to the right computers. A router routes 'packets' of information.
h) Internet service provider — a telephone company that allows you to connect to the Internet.

Q7 Meatspace means "real life" — i.e. where people meet face to face instead of on Internet messageboards and in chatrooms. It's the opposite of cyberspace, and it comes from a comic strip published on the Internet.

Q8 any reasonable answer

## *Page 23*

Q1 or so Edith thought

Q2 b) being explicit

Q3 The word 'ill' actually means the opposite, because Steve was not ill, he just didn't want to take the spelling test.

Q4 a) irony or being ironic

Q5 Any sensible answers, e.g.
a) Marvin is the king of punctuality.
b) Fiona's mum has been known to take a while to get to her destination.
c) Oh, thank you so much for your wise contribution!
d) Sharilyn isn't challenged by the demands of a hectic social life.

## Section Three
## Sentences and Paragraphs

## *Page 24*

Q1 a) I'll tidy up my room, if I can ever find the time.
b) There was a lull in the fighting, so I ran like mad for cover.
c) There was never a dull moment, when my aunty was behind the wheel.
d) What chance was there of survival, given that all the life jackets were missing?
e) You know that dinner is ready, when the microwave explodes into flames.

Q2, Q3: any reasonable answers

## *Page 25*

Q1, Q2: any reasonable answers

Q3 any reasonable answers, but the types of sentence should be as follows:
a) short – should be eye-catching and short enough for people to read as they walk or drive past.
b) detailed – need to make the reader want to stay in the hotel.
c) short – should be eye-catching and short enough for people to read as they walk or drive past.
d) short – have to be able to read it as quickly as possible.
e) detailed – need to give the reader enough information to make them want to see the film.

Q4 any reasonable answer

## *Page 26*

Q1 a) How can you say that? They ate his brains!
b) Is this legal? Where is the emergency stop button?
c) That is a dead hamster! What is the meaning of this?
d) When can I go home? Look out, it's the police!

Q2 any reasonable answers

Q3 a) "I'll tell you something else you don't know: that I hate rice pudding."
b) "Paul often gets confused: last week he spread shoe polish on his toast and shined his shoes with butter."
c) "I'll tell you how the other team beat us so easily: they cheated from start to finish."
d) The brain surgeon had something much more important on his mind:

his hot date with the nurse from reception.

Q4 any reasonable answer

## *Page 27*

Q1 a) "I couldn't talk; I was driving in the motorway fast lane at ninety miles per hour."
b) "That was the most exciting World Cup game I'd ever seen."
c) "The suspect left the building via the underground car park."
d) "I found it hard to breathe and couldn't concentrate properly."
e) "Where was the light switch? The room was in total darkness."

Q2 a) I don't know what is happening.
b) We have found her phone in the cloakroom.
c) I have been walking all day and night.
d) The game has just finished.
e) I'm having a lovely holiday.
f) She's been unhappy for a while.
g) I love her.
h) The explosion has destroyed everything.
i) The lesson is really boring.
Note: there are alternative answers to some of the above.

Q3 a) will, be b) will c) shall/will d) going, to e) will, be

Q4 any reasonable answer

## *Page 28*

Q1, Q2, Q3: any reasonable answers

Q4 The paragraph should read as follows: If I were to go on holiday, I would go to California. The weather would be so hot and sunny that it would be a crime not to spend a lot of time sunbathing on the beach. I would do so many exciting things. But swimming with sharks would have to be the best. It would be the best holiday I would ever have had.

## *Page 29*

Q1 The paragraph should read as follows: We watched the bank closely for a week, getting to know the security guard's routine. We disguised ourselves as nuns, to conceal our true identities. We entered the bank at twelve o'clock midday and forced everyone to lie on the ground. Dave D. Dangerous blew open the main vault, using his special mix of nitroglycerine and alcohol. We put the money into bags under our robes and exited the building calmly, one by one.

# The Answers

Q2, Q3, Q4: any reasonable answers

## Page 30

Q1 any reasonable answer
e.g. a) The referee controls the game that the footballer is playing in.

Q2 a) no b) yes c) no d) no e) yes

Q3, Q4: any reasonable answers

## Section Four
## Types of Non-Fiction

## Page 31

Q1 a) geography
b) history
c) science (biology)
d) mathematics
e) design and technology

Q2 any reasonable answers

Q3 any reasonable answers, e.g.
try to use formal language — do not use slang
make the tone less chatty
include important facts: dates, place names etc.
try to be neutral
write in well structured sentences
etc.

Q4 any reasonable answer

## Page 32

Q1 any reasonable answers

Q2 any reasonable answers

Q3 any reasonable answer

Q4 any reasonable answer, e.g.
a) editorial
b) advertisement
c) documentary

Q5 any reasonable answer

## Page 33

Q1 a) i) first person
ii) third person
iii) first person
iv) third person
b) i) present
ii) past
iii) past
iv) present

Q2 any reasonable answers, e.g.
a) They were under attack.
b) He / she was very sorry.

c) Their hands were tied.
d) He / she trusted Jack completely.

Q3 a) The poem was written by Anna.
b) You were seen by him.
c) I was bitten by an evil little elf.
d) We were caught by the teacher.

Q4 any reasonable answer

## Section Five
## Varieties of English

## Page 34

Q1 Standard English: a, d, e
Regional dialect: b, c, f

Q2 Use standard English: a, c, d, e

Q3 any reasonable answer — for example:
b) I would like three glasses of lemonade, and also two bags of beetroot flavoured crisps, please.
c) The criminal said that he had neither stolen the car nor any other property, but the judge did not believe a word he said and he sentenced the man to five years in prison.
d) Vincent van Gogh was a very famous painter who, in a state of great distress due to a disappointment in love, cut off one of his ears.

Q4 True: a, b, c
False: d

## Page 35

Q1 formal: a, c, d, f, h, i
informal: b, e, g

Q2 any reasonable answers

Q3 a) very formal
b) very informal
c) fairly informal
d) fairly informal / very informal
e) quite formal

Q4 any reasonable answers

Q5 any reasonable answer — for example:
I had to drop our Alex off at her school. It was raining heavily so we both got soaked. I decided that I should go home and get changed rather than go to school wet and be uncomfortable. Unfortunately by then the bus had gone, so I had to walk.

## Page 36

Q1 Shakespeare: b, c, d, f, g
Modern: a, e, h

Q2 a) "Shall I compare you to a summer's day? You are more lovely and more calm."
b) "Turn round, Benvolio, and look upon your death."
c) "You villain, Capulet!"
d) "Or else I'd very shortly see you there."
e) "Why do you smile like that, and kiss your hand so often?"

Q3 Dr Vibe's assistant: Thou art dead lucky, Doctor. That titanium plate in thy bonce deflected the laser blast away from the dead centre of thy tremendously powerful but devious brain.
Dr Vibe: What dost thou mean, thou cringing assistant? What art thou saying?
Dr Vibe's cringing assistant: I mean to say that thy life is no longer under threat. And the foul Professor Pertang wilt never endanger thy plans again.
Dr Vibe: Yippee! Pass me thy pack of powerful peppermints. I feel like celebrating. In fact, cringing assistant, thou canst give the cat a mint too.

Q4 True: a, c, d
False: b, e

## Page 37

Q1 a) Le porc — pork
b) Le veau — veal
c) Le boeuf — beef
d) Le beurre — butter
e) La fleur — flower

Q2 a) Dear Mark
I am asking for your help. I want to get much better with my English. Please study my writing and then send me a reply. I would very much like to improve my writing of English sentences. Will you write back to me soon with your suggestions? Did you watch the Man United match on the television?
Love Jan
b) German main verbs are often placed at the very end of the sentence — unlike English.

Q3 a) Dear Trish
I hope you are well. Thank you very much for your letter; I found it on the doormat when I got home from school. School — I do not like it so much at the moment. I am having to read an English book at the moment — I find it very difficult and I do not like it! But I love your English pop music!

# The Answers

I have just bought a new CD by The X-Ray Mutant Radio Gang — it is an excellent disc!"
Love Colette

b) In French all nouns (names of things) are either masculine or feminine.

Q4  a)  Italian
     b)  French
     c)  Italian
     d)  French
     e)  Italian
     f)  French

## Section Six
## Research and Study Skills

## Page 38

Q1  any reasonable answer

## Page 39

Q1  From context:
a 'whizzbit' could either be a ball or puck of some kind, or alternatively a name for a 'shot' or 'volley'.
A 'fredu' seems to be a type of bat or racquet.

Q2  any reasonable answer

Q3  'railstrom' means 'team'. It appears in exactly the same context as the word 'team' as we use it today e.g. 'railstrom effort'.

Q4  any reasonable answer

## Page 40

Q1  iv)

Q2  any reasonable answer, e.g.
1. two men with rifles entered bank
2. girl lets down tyres on getaway car
3. thieves are caught

Q3  any reasonable answer

Q4  any reasonable answers

## Page 41

Q1  No. The writer is also asking for somewhere to be provided for young people to go in the evening.

Q2  The tone of the letter suggests that the writer is more concerned about getting the young people away from their house than helping them. The letter suggests that kids being on the streets is a problem because it 'upsets' the writer.

Q3  any reasonable answers including:
The resident is annoyed by youths gathering outside their house.
The youths are not agressive — just bored.
Facilities must be provided for them.

Q4  any reasonable answers
one possible solution would be a youth club

## Page 42

Q1  Source 1:
Richard has his own society.
Members dress in medieval clothes and listen to music of the time.
Richard lost at Bosworth.
Source 2:
Play was written about 100 years after Richard died.
Shakespeare worked for the Tudors.
The Tudors defeated Richard.
Source 3:
Richard ruled between 1483 and 1485.
He married Anne Neville.
He had one son who died in 1484.
He had one illegitimate daughter called Kathryn.
He toured the country as king.
He was defeated at Bosworth in 1485.

Q2  Source 1:
Richard was a great king, and innocent of the crimes he has since been accused of.
Source 2:
Richard was a murderous, scheming villain.
Source 3:
No obvious opinion.

Q3  Either 2,1,3 or 1,2,3. This is open to debate.

Q4  Source 3 could be helpful to a historian, since it is as impartial as possible.

Q5  No — all history is selective and coloured by opinion.

## Page 43

Q1  a)  sarcastic
     b)  sarcastic
     c)  not sarcastic
     d)  sarcastic
     e)  not sarcastic

Q2  a)  ironic
     b)  ironic
     c)  not ironic
     d)  not ironic (just dumb really)
     e)  ironic

Q3  any reasonable answer

## Page 44

Q1  v)

Q2  a)  with tone of voice
     b)  by following Bob round and getting to know him
     c)  with melodramatic close-ups, expressions and poses
     d)  with facial expressions

Q3  any reasonable answer

Q4  any reasonable answer

## Page 45

Q1  a)  heavy traffic
     b)  thunderstorm
     c)  baby crying
     d)  birds singing
     e)  police siren

Q2  any reasonable answers

Q3  any reasonable answer

Q4  any reasonable answer

Q5  any reasonable answer

## Section Seven
## Author's Craft

## Page 46

Q1  a)  autobiography
     b)  crime fiction
     c)  satire
     d)  historical chronicle
     e)  lyric poetry
     f)  gothic horror

Q2  a)  A is the introduction
         B is the conclusion
     b)  any reasonable answer — for example:
A gives more of an explanation of what they're doing and who Jane is. It also ends with a cliffhanger.
B ends quietly and calmly, with no indication that something else may happen. The text also assumes we know who Jane is, so it's more likely to be a conclusion.

## Page 47

Q1  a bird (of some sort)

Q2  a)  true
     b)  true
     c)  false

# The Answers

d) false
e) true
f) false
g) true

3 any reasonable answer

## Section Eight
## Literary Texts

### Page 48

1 answers may vary slightly:
a) loves the sea
b) fears the sea / sailing
c) dislikes sailing

2 In extract A, the sea is described as 'a great beast, mighty but gentle'
In extract B, a 'storm howled' around the ship.
In extract C, hailstones 'fell in showers, coldest of grains' on the ship. The route they take across the sea is called the 'whale-road'.

3, Q4: any reasonable answers

### Page 49

1 a) fourteen, quatrains
b) monster
c) happily
d) exaggerate
e) narrative
f) in tears

2 any reasonable answer

3 a) ii
b) iv
c) i
d) iii

### Page 50

1 a) Captain Peleg
b) ii (a whaling boat)
c) The Pequod
d) Ahab's leg was eaten by a whale.

2 a) ii (fairly flat and boring)
b) no — they have cracked roofs.
c) answers may vary slightly:
the graveyards are run down and the churches are falling to pieces.

## Section Nine
## Essay Skills

### Page 51

1 The correct order is: g, b, f, c, a, e, d.

---

Q2 to Q5: any reasonable answer

### Page 52

Q1 any reasonable answers

Q2 a) newspaper report
b) fairy story
c) legal document
d) letter
e) poem

Q3 any reasonable answer

Q4 any reasonable answers

### Page 53

Q1 to Q3: any reasonable answers

### Page 54

Q1 proportions as shown on page

Q2 all letters should be the same height

Q3 to Q6: the sentence should be written in a joined hand, obeying the rules from Q1.

## Section Ten
## Writing Fiction

### Page 55

Q1 a) third person
b) first person
c) third person
d) first person
e) second person

Q2 a) matches ii)
b) matches iii)
c) matches i)

Q3 b) This is in the second person but should be in the first:
Dear diary, I have had such a terrible day. First I had a terrible fight with my mum and then I was late for school.
c) This is in the first person but should be in the second:
Scorpio
You have been having a bad time recently. You need to slow down and take stock of your life. Pluto in your solar house is making you feel sluggish and you should pamper yourself until you feel better.

Q4 a) first person
b) third person
c) either first or third person

---

d) second person
e) third person

### Page 56

Q1 a) yes
b) no
c) yes
d) yes
e) no

Q2 any reasonable answers

Q3 a) b) and c) any reasonable answers

Q4 any reasonable answer

### Page 57

Q1 active: a), d), g), h)
passive: b), c), e), f)

Q2 a) passive
b) passive
c) active
d) active
e) passive
f) passive
g) active

Q3 a) The precious vase was broken by Philip.
b) The experiment was carried out on Tuesday.
c) The equipment was damaged.
d) The mosque was built in 1934 by a lot of people.
e) A fake £50 note was used.
f) Carbon monoxide gas was added to the water sample.
g) Anabel was awarded the "most beautiful baby" prize.
h) The old pet shop was set on fire.
i) The police were phoned by the terrified pigs.

### Page 58

Q1 a) i) Snow White and the Seven Dwarves
ii) Jack and the Beanstalk
iii) Little Red Riding Hood
iv) Beauty and the Beast

b) i) to iv): any reasonable answers

Q2 to Q4: any reasonable answers

### Page 59

Q1 to Q3: any reasonable answers

# The Answers

## Section Eleven
## Writing Information

### Page 60

Q1  a)  performance
    b)  entertainment system
    c)  interior features
    d)  bodywork features
    e)  safety
    f)  comfort

Q2  any reasonable answer

Q3  a) ii)  b) i)  c) v)  d) iii)  e) iv)

Q4  any reasonable answer

### Page 61

Q1  the correct order is:  keyboard, monitor, word-process, spellchecker, fonts, graphics, multitasking

Q2  the correct order is:  are caused by, by taking, are the result, are spread by, will spread over, was recorded at

Q3, Q4  any reasonable answers

Q5  a)  I broke the window because I was kicking the ball in the yard.
    b)  I put some spin on the ball so that it was harder for the batsman to strike.
    c)  I taped the components to the side of the model so that they would be held in place until the glue was dry.
    d)  The missile can make decisions as it flies because it is fitted with a computer.

### Page 62

Q1  a) ii)  b) i)  c) iv)  d) v)  e) iii)  f) vi)

Q2  informal:  d), e)
    formal:  a), b), c)

Q3  a) no  b) yes  c) no  d) yes  e) no

Q4  any reasonable answers

## Section Twelve
## Writing To Persuade

### Page 63

Q1  a)  Surely everyone would agree with the idea that children do not receive enough pocket money and that they deserve a huge rise.
    b)  We all know that schoolboys are much cleverer than girls, it's just

that they're extremely modest and don't like to show off their intelligence in lessons.
    c)  Surely no one could disagree with the idea that the fox population is better controlled by more humane methods than hunting.
    d)  We all know that modern pop music is far better and more entertaining than the boring old records our parents used to listen to when they were kids.

Q2  any reasonable answers

Q3  The five sentences are as follows:
    Whales have been hunted close to extinction, as a result / consequently, all hunting of whales must stop now.
    Boys prefer PCs to books, however / nevertheless, there is lots to read on the Internet.
    Bikes are cheaper than cars, moreover, cycling keeps you fitter.
    Climbing is a dangerous sport, nevertheless / however, ropes and other equipment can make it safer.
    Uniforms make everyone look the same, consequently / as a result, all pupils are treated equally.

Q4  any reasonable answers — for example:
    a)  How can you watch a film without a huge tub of popcorn?
    b)  Have you ever met a fish which complained of being hooked out of the water?
    c)  How can you go to Paris and not go to the Eiffel Tower?

### Page 64

Q1  a) i), viii), ix)  b) iv), v)  c) ii), vi)  d) iii), vii)

Q2  any reasonable answers
    Answers should be written in a similar way to the example given.

Q3  a) no  b) yes  c) yes  d) yes  e) no  f) yes  g) yes  h) yes  i) no

### Page 65

Q1  b)  You could pay for the broken window now.  Alternatively, you could wait until you get paid.
    c)  You could go with your friend to offer support.  On the other hand, you could wait outside the Head's room.
    d)  You could wipe out the entire alien race with your laser.  Or you could invite them round for a pizza and a cola.

Q2  (answers may vary)
    b)  Why don't you phone a friend?
    c)  I advise that you don't use the phone for over three hours each evening.

    d)  I suggest that you flatter your dad when you want to break some bad news.

Q3  a)  If you tell your brother that you took his pocket money, then he will understand.
    b)  If you start planning the party two weeks in advance, then the guests are bound to have a great time.
    c)  If you continually put off getting your homework done, then eventually you're going to find it's too late and your teachers will be mad at you.
    d)  If you go around dressed like that, then all the girls are bound to find you irresistibly attractive and Tracy in particular will fall in love with you at the Valentine Disco.
    e)  If you keep on shouting at me like that, then I will simply stop being your friend and you'll be all alone.
    f)  If you eat three chocolate bars before school, then it's not surprising that you feel a bit sick in Maths even when you can do the sums.

## Section Thirteen
## Critical Writing

### Page 66

Q1  any reasonable answer

Q2  a)  evidence
    b)  point
    c)  explanation

Q3, Q4 and Q5:  any reasonable answers

### Page 67

Q1  any reasonable answer — for example:
    i)  "in case you lot out there in reality land had forgotten"
    ii)  "I won't tell you any more in case spoil the plot for you;"
    iii)  "buy it before the film comes out!"

Q2  any reasonable answer — for example:
    a)  "dastardly Dursleys" or "funny, frightening"
    b)  "I won't tell you any more"
    c)  "Hogwarts school is simply a creation of genius."
    d)  "buy it before the film comes out"

Q3  any reasonable answer

Q4  a)  implication
    b)  statement
    c)  statement
    d)  statement
    e)  implication
    f)  implication